14 Days to Sustainable Happiness

a workbook for every brain

Loretta Breuning, PhD

Inner Mammal Institute

CONTENTS

page

This book is dedicated to
the many readers who give me
valuable feedback.
They remind me every day that
we're all mammals!

MORE BOOKS BY

Loretta Graziano Breuning, PhD

Habits of a Happy Brain
Retrain Your Brain to Boost Your Serotonin,
Dopamine, Oxytocin and Endorphin Levels

Status Games
Why We Play and How to Stop

Tame Your Anxiety
Rewiring Your Brain for Happiness

The Science of Positivity
Stop Negative Thought Patterns by Changing
Your Brain Chemistry

Preface

A NEW VIEW OF HAPPINESS

This workbook helps you find your power over your happy brain chemicals: dopamine, serotonin, oxytocin, and endorphin. It's a step-by-step program that tells you what stimulates good feelings, and how to get more of them. There is no fast, easy way, it must be said. But you can learn sustainable ways to turn on your happy chemicals and replace any unsustainable happy habits you may already have.

Most important, you will build realistic expectations. Our happy chemicals are not meant to flow all the time. They evolved to reward you for taking steps to meet your needs. Small steps are enough as long as you keep taking them. In the next two weeks, you will learn to take realistic steps and enjoy the happy-chemical rewards.

This new approach is rooted in basic biology. More complete explanations of the science can be found in my book: **Habits of a Happy Brain: Retrain your brain to boost your serotonin, dopamine, oxytocin and endorphin levels.** This workbook is a companion to that book.

Our happy chemicals are controlled by neural pathways built from past experience. This book helps you discover your unique neural pathways and your

power to build new ones. There is no right way to happiness because each brain is wired from its own lived experience. Each of us must manage the brain we have. You can feel good by understanding the wiring you've built and adding to it as needed. You can't do this if you're focused on the wiring of others, which is why this book has few examples. If you are eager for examples, turn to Day 14 (the happy ending!).

You can use this workbook alone or with professional counseling. You might use it with a group so you can discuss your responses to the exercises with others. You could even create your own Inner Mammal Support Group. Dr. Breuning will do a free Q&A with your group on completion of the 14 days. Contact her at: innermammalinstitute.org.

The method presented in this book is not affiliated with any religion, therapy, or philosophy. It is only based on the work of the Inner Mammal Institute. Each reader will mesh the new information with their existing beliefs in their own way.

What is the Inner Mammal Institute?

It's not really about animals.

It's not about happiness as your verbal brain defines it.

It's about the happy brain chemicals we've inherited from earlier mammals: dopamine, serotonin, oxytocin, and endorphin. These chemicals are designed to do a job, not to flow all the time. When you know how they work in animals, you can find healthy ways to stimulate yours. You can train your mammal brain and your verbal brain to work together. Find many free resources to help you do that at: innermammalinstitute.org .

Nothing is wrong with you! Nothing is wrong with us! We're mammals.

Disclaimers:
This book is not intended as medical treatment.
Nothing in this book is intended to support breaking the law. The rule of law benefits all of us.

YOUR POWER OVER YOUR BRAIN

Today you will learn:
o **why everyone has ups and downs**
o **how we produce our feelings**
o **how to find your power over your emotions**

When you feel good, your brain is releasing a happy brain chemical: dopamine, serotonin, oxytocin, or endorphin. We want these great feelings all the time, but our happy chemicals don't work that way. They're designed to do a job, and when you know the job, you can find healthy ways to stimulate them. You will find sustainable paths to happy chemicals, and repeat them until they feel natural. You can avoid unsustainable paths to happy chemicals – behaviors that feel good in the short run but hurt you in the long run.

It shouldn't be so hard, you may say. It seems like others get happy chemicals easily. The truth is, they do not. The brain evolved to promote survival, not to make you happy. It saves the happy chemicals for moments when they help meet a survival need. It releases unhappy chemicals when you see threats to meeting a need. But our brain defines "needs" in a quirky way. Those quirks are the subject of today's lesson.

We humans have two brains– a cortex that's unique to humans and a *limbic system* that's almost the same in all mammals. This mammal brain controls the chemicals that make us feel good and bad. It cannot

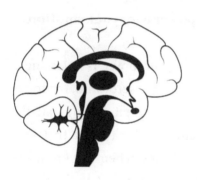

process language, so it cannot tell you why it is releasing a chemical. The human cortex controls language and abstract thought, but it cannot control your chemicals. Our two brains are literally not on speaking terms, and that's why our emotions are so hard to make sense of.

Your mammal brain sees things as a matter of life or death because it evolved to promote survival. Your verbal brain tries to come up with "good reasons" for these responses. It's not easy being a big-brained mammal!

We have two brains because we need both. Do not assume your animal brain is the bad guy. Do not think your human cortex is the bad guy. Each brain has an essential job. When they work together, you can find good ways to feel good. You can help your two brains work together like a horse and rider. You can make

peace with your inner mammal by giving it what it needs in safe, healthy ways.

Research on animals helps us understand what triggers happy chemicals in our lower brain. This week, you'll find out what triggers an animal's dopamine, serotonin, oxytocin, and endorphin, as well as their threat chemical, cortisol. You will see how these chemicals are controlled by old neural pathways. Next week, you'll be ready to find your own pathways and your power to rewire them.

Humans and animals differ in important ways. Creatures with smaller brains are more hard-wired at birth. They leave home at a young age because they're already wired with the survival skills of their ancestors. Bigger-brained creatures have longer childhoods because they build survival skills from lived experience instead of being born with them. **Your wiring was built from your own early experience. You don't consciously think about your childhood when you take steps to meet your needs, but each brain relies on the wiring it has.**

No one's wiring is perfect because childhood experience cannot be a perfect guide to adult challenges. We all need to update our wiring at times. When you know how to do that, you have power over your emotions.

You may be thinking that emotions are completely different from survival skills. But if you think of emotions as nature's GPS, life makes sense. **They tell you to go forward toward rewards by releasing a good feeling, and to retreat from harm by releasing a bad feeling. In the animal world, things that feel good are good for you.** In today's world, it's complicated, but it helps to know that the operating system we've inherited motivates survival action by making it feel good.

Our distant ancestors had to seek food constantly to survive. They were happy when they found something good to eat. The food soon ran out, so they were always looking for more. Happy chemicals motivated them to repeat behaviors that made them happy before. **We have inherited a brain that searches for things that felt good before.** This creates problems in the modern world, where things that feel good are not necessarily good for your survival. **Your emotions in the short-run are not necessarily a good guide to your long-term well-being.**

But you can't just ignore your emotions either. Your verbal brain can't spark action, though it can talk about action endlessly. Your two brains have to work together for you to take steps that meet your needs.

Happy chemicals are like paving on your neural pathways. Whatever felt good in your past paved a pathway that turns on that chemical faster in similar situations today. Unhappy chemicals pave pathways too. This is why we're all unique individuals and there's no one recipe for happiness. But everyone can stimulate their happy chemicals in healthy ways. Everyone can accept their own wiring, design new wiring, and blaze new trails through their jungle of neurons.

We all have a lot in common despite our uniqueness. We all crave happy chemicals because that's how our brain is designed to work. We all get frustrated because our happy chemicals turn on and off for reasons that are hard to make sense of. And we all have the power to build new neural pathways by repeating new thoughts or behaviors.

There is no free happy chemical in the animal world. A critter works hard for any dopamine, serotonin, or oxytocin they get, and threat chemicals fill their lives. **The mammal brain releases happy chemicals in short spurts, so you always have to do more to get more. The chemicals are quickly metabolized, so every good feeling is soon over. The animal brain is designed to keep motivating you to take that next step. It is not designed to make you feel good about sitting on the couch.**

Steps that feel good now could be bad for you later. When later comes, bad consequences motivate you to find a way to feel better. Then you try to stimulate the happy chemical in ways you know, so more bad consequences are likely. You can end up in a bad loop. Fortunately, you can escape this loop by learning sustainable ways to stimulate happy chemicals.

The brain releases happy chemicals when it sees a way to promote survival, but it defines survival in quirky ways. Here are five of our biggest quirks.

#1

Our brain cares about the survival of its genes

You don't consciously care about your genes, and animals don't either. But natural selection built a brain that rewards gene-spreading behaviors with happy chemicals. Those behaviors include: love, lust, nurturing offspring, finding allies, protecting turf, the ever-popular quest to look good, and a thirst for gossip about who likes who. We do these things because our brain makes them feel good. But the mammal brain can't explain why, so your verbal brain comes up with clever explanations for why you do them. It may seem hard to believe that gene-spreading behaviors spark your happy chemicals. It helps to know that survival rates were very low in the state of nature. You are here today because your ancestors did what it took to keep their genes alive. We are all descended from survivors!

Social skills help spread your genes in the mammal world. It's tempting to define social skills in a romanticized way, but our mammal brain rewards what works. Asserting yourself works. Building alliances works. Whatever helped our ancestors survive is what the mammal brain rewards. And that's why you feel good when you succeed at asserting yourself or building alliances.

Any obstacle to spreading your genes is a survival threat from your mammal brain's perspective. That's why your threat chemicals react so strongly to a bad hair day, a friend who doesn't return your call, or your child's problem in school. You don't consciously see these frustrations as threats to the survival of your genes, but you have inherited the brain that kept your ancestors alive.

#2

Our brain focuses on un-met needs

A survival brain doesn't waste happy chemicals on the same old thing. It saves them for the moment when you satisfy an un-met need. If your ancestors found a fruit tree and stuffed themselves with fruit, the good feeling would soon stop because that need was met. Then, finding protein would spark their happy chemicals because that nutritional need was not met. The mammal brain takes what you have for granted and saves the happy chemicals for new ways to promote your survival.

You don't think this consciously, of course. Your brain simply *habituates* to an input. For example, you may love the smell of a flower, but taping a flower to your nose won't make you happy because you soon stop noticing it. Your brain is designed to scan the world for new information about meeting your needs.

If you were thirsty in the desert, you'd be thrilled by a sign of water in the distance. But unlimited water does not make you happy today because that need is already met. **This is why people focus on what they don't have, despite their best intentions.**

The flaws of this mindset are obvious, so you may insist that we shouldn't think this way. But your brain does think this way, so you are better off understanding it. In the modern world, physical needs are more easily met, so social needs tend to spark more happy chemicals. The result is that small social ups and downs trigger big emotions.

#3

Our brain confuses the past with the present

Each brain sees the world through a lens built by its own past experience. A newborn baby has no experience, so it has no survival skills, even though its brain is gigantic compared to earlier mammals. A new brain cannot make sense of the world until its neurons connect from repeated activation. The good feelings you experienced in the past built connections that tell you where to expect good feelings today.

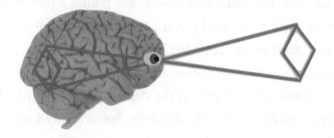

Past experience is not a perfect guide to the future, of course. Eating ice cream felt good in my past, but constantly seeking ice cream would not be a sustainable path to a happy future. My brain expects good feelings from ice cream, however, because pathways build from experience.

Fortunately, the big human cortex can transform past experience into predictions about the future. I can predict what will happen if I eat too much ice cream. I can predict other ways to feel good. But I need experience to build pathways that make such predictions. Otherwise, I would just keep eating ice cream.

Animals take the past as a good guide to the future. Past experience with food guides an animal toward future food, and past experience with predators helps them avoid future predators. Animals are often wrong, in fact, but they don't second guess themselves. We humans want to avoid error and improve. But the pathways built from our past are very efficient so it's hard to let go of them.

#4

Your brain mirrors others

We don't intend to mirror others, but *mirror neurons* do it without conscious intent. When you see someone get a reward, your mirror neurons trigger the same pathway you'd activate if you got the reward yourself. When you see someone face a threat, your mirror neurons trigger that sense of threat in you. Mirrored sensations are much weaker than direct experience, but repeated activation builds a pathway. The mammal brain is designed to learn from experience, so if you witness certain rewards or threats repeatedly, you get wired to respond to those rewards and threats.

Mirror neurons allow animals to learn skills by watching without the need for talking. Mirror neurons taught our ancestors to run from predators when others ran, and find food in ways that worked for others. Your habits are shaped by what you've mirrored more than you realize.

Your brain perceives its own mortality

Your mammal brain cares urgently about survival, but your human brain knows you will fail in your quest to survive someday. Death is an abstraction, and only the human cortex can process abstractions. We humans see the inevitability of our own demise. This is why we constantly scan for potential future threats, whereas animals only notice threats once they're up close. We humans improve our lives by anticipating threats in time to prevent them, but we also terrorize ourselves with our own threat-seeking. What a quirk!

This is why we're always eager for relief from threatened feelings. Unfortunately, many threat-relievers are not sustainable. They bring short-run relief in ways that threaten you in the long run. Fortunately, there's a sustainable alternative: imagining your own legacy. Happy chemicals are stimulated when you think your unique individual essence will survive once your body is gone. It sounds pretentious, but pondering your legacy eases your mammalian survival fear. This is why people are so eager to create things that will last after they're gone.

MAKE IT HAPPEN

These exercises help you find your power over your happy brain chemicals.

o **Notice strong feelings you have about things relevant to the survival of your genes: your appearance, your relatives, and your social alliances.**

_____

_____

_____

o **Notice how you get excited about something new, and stop getting excited about what you already have.**

_____

_____

o **Find a match between a good experience in your past and something that makes you happy today. What matters is the overall pattern, not the surface details.**

_____

_____

_____

THE JOY OF DOPAMINE

Today you will learn:
- o **what turns on the joy of dopamine**
- o **why we don't have it all the time**
- o **how it's wired from past experience**

When you're excited, your brain is releasing dopamine. You want this great feeling all the time, but dopamine isn't meant to surge all the time. It's your brain's signal that you're about to meet a need. It turns on when you get something good, or anticipate something good. Your brain decides what's good in an interesting way. Neurons connect when dopamine flows, which wires you to turn on the good feeling easily when you see something that triggered it before. You don't think this consciously with your verbal brain. It's just electricity flowing into a path that exists.

To your conscious mind, the pleasures of your youth may seem juvenile. But if you look at what excites you today, you will see core patterns from your past. It's easier to see how this works in animals because they are non-verbal.

Imagine you're a little monkey waking up hungry. You don't have a refrigerator or a supermarket, so how

 do you relieve your hunger? You look around, and your dopamine surges when you see a piece of fruit. The good feeling tells you to go toward that, and each step closer triggers more dopamine. Once you get the fruit, the dopamine stops because it has already done its job. You won't get more until you meet a need again, and you are eager to do that because dopamine makes it feel good.

A monkey doesn't understand its nutritional needs. It just learns from experience that finding food feels good. When you were born, you didn't understand your needs in a cognitive way, but each time a need was met, dopamine wired you to expect a good feeling from similar experiences. Animals work

harder for food than you may think. A monkey chooses branches that can hold its weight so it doesn't fall to the ground and get eaten by a predator. Dopamine rewards it for each successful step. Neurons connect, and wire a little monkey to meet its needs by doing things it expects to feel good. Your dopamine got wired by expectations too.

Dopamine releases energy to fuel the chase. It gives a lion the surge of energy it needs to catch a gazelle. We enjoy this energy, so we long for dopamine. But **if it flowed constantly, it would not promote survival.** A lion with constant dopamine would run after every gazelle and its energy would be used up by the time it saw one it could catch. Instead, a lion's brain saves the dopamine for a good prospect, as defined by its own past experience. Dopamine helps a monkey decide which fruit is worth climbing for, and which fruit is best ignored. Your brain saves the dopamine for good prospects too.

Dopamine creates the "I can get it!" feeling. It's easy to see why we crave this feeling, but also why we don't always have it. Dopamine helps us invest our energy where it is most likely to get rewards. Our inner mammal decides this without words because the electricity in the brain flows easily along pathways that were activated before. When you see a pattern of cues that match a past success, your electricity flows to the "on" switch of your dopamine. The good feeling tells you to invest energy now.

Dopamine turns on before you actually meet a need, thanks to old pathways. It gives you advance notice so you have time to take effective action. **Dopamine creates the sense of anticipation that says "this is going to be good!" That motivates you to invest the effort necessary to reach a reward.**

Mirror neurons help to shape our dopamine pathways. A baby monkey mirrors its mother when she grabs food. It puts things in its mouth before it knows what food is. The brain releases dopamine when it tastes sugar or fat because they meet its needs. The good feeling motivates another bite. Young monkeys are never fed except for mother's milk. They only get solids if they take action, but every monkey learns thanks to dopamine.

You may insist that you don't care about survival or rewards because you are motivated by higher values. But your mammal brain is always looking for ways to feel good with pathways built by your dopamine past.

When you take steps toward dopamine, you don't always get what you expect. Sometimes you get more and sometimes less. Getting less triggers the bad feeling of cortisol, which we explore on Day 6. Getting more triggers a big dopamine surge. This builds a big pathway that helps you find more big rewards. A friend of mine once got two chocolate milks from a vending machine when she only paid for one. This happened decades ago, but she remembers it every time she walks near that machine. She understood why when she learned about dopamine.

What if rewards are exactly as you expected rather than more or less? This is the tricky part of life. Our brain stops releasing dopamine when there's no new information. We habituate to expected rewards. My first tiramisu thrilled me with dopamine, but soon the thrill was gone. You can only discover a new pleasure once. I still love tiramisu because the pathway is there, and because sugar and fat are scarce in the state of nature. But if I expect the surge of the first time, I will be disappointed.

Habituation makes life challenging! We love the dopamine of hitting the jackpot. But we get wired to expect that feeling, even though jackpots are rare. This is why life often disappoints. And it's why people get hooked on gambling or pizza or pornography or success or other triggers of jackpot feelings.

Dopamine has gotten a bad reputation as a result. Yet we need it to function in daily life. Dopamine makes it possible to read this page. Your brain searches for a match between the letters you see and the meanings you've learned to associate with them. Each match triggers a bit of dopamine, and the good feeling moves you on to the next word. You do this so smoothly that you don't even notice, but if you spend time with a six-year-old, you see how the joy of finding meaning gets wired. Let's look closer at how dopamine helps us navigate daily life.

When you were born, you didn't know what milk is and you didn't know what a mother is. But in a few days, dopamine had wired you to anticipate a good feeling when you heard your mother's footsteps. Experience linked certain sights and sounds to the good feeling of having your needs met. A few months later, dopamine motivated you to crawl toward a toy. The toy did not meet an immediate survival need, but it was something different, and seeking something different promotes survival in the state of nature. So your brain released dopamine and you went for it. You didn't know how to crawl, but you kept trying because dopamine was released each time you got closer. You would not have enjoyed that dopamine if someone put the toy in your hand. Early experience teaches us to stimulate good feelings with our own actions.

A new toy stops triggering dopamine once it becomes familiar. So you look for something new, and your brain rewards you with dopamine.

What if you see a new toy in another child's hands? Dopamine motivates you to seek it. If you grab it away, an adult may be there to make you give it back. Slowly over time, we learn better ways to seek rewards.

Dopamine didn't evolve for seeking toys, of course. It evolved to guide you to meet your needs. Your brain knows a need has been met when a bad feeling is relieved. Food relieves the bad feeling of hunger. Warmth relieves the bad feeling of cold. Your brain releases dopamine whenever you relieve a bad feeling, and that wires you to expect relief in ways that worked before.

We define relief without conscious thought. For example, a baboon can save itself from a lion by climbing a tree, and that wires it to scan for trees the next time it smells a threat. **When you feel threatened, you scan for things that brought you relief before.** The bigger the threat, the more dopamine you enjoy when you relieve it. For example, imagine you get lost in the woods on a camping trip. You go hungry all day, and when you finally find your campsite, you eat a peanut butter sandwich. It tastes better than the finest meal, though you're not sure why.

In the modern world, the lessons you learn from dopamine don't always make sense. Imagine that you

flunk a math test, and then play a video game when you leave the classroom. Dopamine is stimulated by the game because it creates the illusion that you are approaching a reward. You feel good, even though the real problem is not solved. Neurons connect, and the next time you face a math test, you have a strong urge to play a video game.

You would not survive in the state of nature if you played video games instead of taking effective steps to meet your needs. But in the modern world, your survival needs will be met by someone else if you keep playing. Each time you choose the video game, you strengthen your brain's expectation that gaming is the way to feel good. It doesn't meet your long-run needs, of course, so you end up with more math stress. If you don't understand your brain, you respond with more gaming.

Instead, you could build a new pathway that expects rewards from studying. That may seem like a Catch-22 since you don't know how to expect that. Fortunately, small steps are enough to stimulate dopamine as long as you see yourself approaching a reward. If you take small steps toward your math goal, repeatedly, a new pathway will build. To ease the process, you can give yourself immediate rewards when you take steps that bring long-term rewards.

A reward for each study session would train your brain to associate studying with good feelings. **Immediate rewards help you get started when you don't already have positive expectations. But if you reward yourself for pretending to study without actually studying, you get wired to expect rewards from pretending.**

You can blaze a new trail in your brain to get rewards in new ways. If you don't, you will keep repeating whatever dopamine habits you've learned. And you won't know why, since we're not aware of our own pathways. Your verbal brain will try to explain your choices. It will blame your math class. It's hard to accept the power of old pathways over our feelings, expectations, and actions.

If you get a good grade in math, a big dopamine spurt will strengthen your new pathway. But if you get the same good grade on every test, your dopamine will not surge each time. You just expect it once the pathway forms. But you may look for a new challenge because you have wired yourself to expect good feelings from your own actions.

The mammal brain promotes survival by rewarding you with dopamine when you act to relieve

 a threat. Our ancestors needed firewood to survive in the winter, and dopamine made them feel good when they found it. The colder it was and the scarcer the firewood, the happier it made them.

Today, it's easier to keep warm, but that doesn't make you happy. You habituate to the comforts you have and look for new ways to enjoy dopamine. This is why meeting social needs gets our attention. The following chapters explain how social rewards trigger serotonin and oxytocin. Dopamine is always involved because it rewards you for taking action to get a social reward or relieve a social threat. Any success wires you to expect more rewards from similar steps.

When you feel excited about something, it's because you connected it to meeting a need or relieving a threat in your past. We get excited about different things because different experiences wire in different expectations. Maybe you expect a promotion to meet your needs, so dopamine rewards you for taking steps toward a promotion. Maybe you expect another cocktail to meet your needs, so your dopamine rewards you for finding a bar that's open. Maybe you expect a new outfit to meet your needs, so your dopamine surges when you shop, or apply for a higher credit limit. **Many paths to dopamine are not sustainable. They hurt you in the long run even though they feel good in the short run. The big human cortex can think about the long run, but your mammal brain is still eager for immediate dopamine. Your two brains have to work together to find sustainable paths to dopamine.**

Don't jump to the conclusion that the mammal brain is the problem. The verbal brain plays a big role in our unsustainable choices. If you choose to play video games instead of studying, your verbal brain comes up with an explanation that makes you look good. If you choose to have another drink or buy another outfit or chase another promotion, your verbal brain finds a way to make it sound like "the right thing." It's hard to believe we do things because neurons connected long ago. When you see the patterns, it's easier to rewire them.

We are born with billions of neurons but almost no connections between them. You'd be as helpless as

a newborn without the connections you've built. You can also build new connections, but it takes your full attention. That makes it impossible to do other things at the same time. For example, you can drive and talk at the same time because old pathways guide you, but if you try to speak a new language while driving on a new road, watch out! No wonder we rely on old pathways so much.

You will build new connections if you invest your attention in a new thought or behavior for a few minutes a day. Day 7 helps you discover your old dopamine circuits, and Day 11 helps you build new additions. Today, your goal is to notice the motivating power of dopamine in the world around you. Each of us has our own path to dopamine, but our paths are similar because they're wired in youth when we have limited insight into our long-run needs. This is the challenge of being human!

MAKE IT HAPPEN

The quest for dopamine is a huge motivator in daily life. These exercises help you notice the power of dopamine in the world around you.

o **Notice the excitement you feel when you see a new way to meet a need. When does that good feeling stop?**

_____

_____

_____

o **Notice other people getting excited about an expected reward and taking steps toward it.**

_____

_____

_____

o **Find examples of people seeking an instant reward to relieve a bad feeling.**

_____

_____

_____

Day 3

THE SAFETY OF OXYTOCIN

Today you will learn:
- to notice the feeling that it's safe to lower your guard
- the way oxytocin makes you feel good when you find social support
- why oxytocin doesn't flow all the time

A gazelle finds it hard to eat when it's alone because it has to scan constantly for predators. Being with a herd allows it to lower its guard and enjoy the grass. It feels safe because the burden of monitoring for threats is shared. Oxytocin creates that nice, safe feeling. It's released when you expect protection from others.

But you don't want to follow the herd all the time. Their horns get in your way and they pee on your food. You want your space and independence. The problem is that oxytocin falls when you distance yourself from the safety of social support. It feels bad. What's a mammal to do?

A gazelle is always choosing between a step toward the herd and a step toward greener pastures. It chooses between the oxytocin of social support and the dopamine of fresh grass. The dopamine is  tempting, but an isolated mammal is quickly seized by predators. So the good feeling of oxytocin is its reward for playing it safe. Natural selection built a brain that promotes survival by rewarding you with oxytocin when you find social support.

But it's complicated. Life in a herd is not all warm and fuzzy. You have to run whenever the herd runs, even though there are lots of false alarms. You have to monitor the group constantly so you don't get left behind. This is why a teenager feels devastated if everybody hangs out without them. Staying connected takes a lot of effort, but mammals do it because isolation feels like a survival threat.

A gazelle seeks its own herd for maximum protection. If it runs to the wrong herd in a moment of threat, they might not let it in. Mammals are quite picky about who is in their herd. They want allies who are willing and able to protect them. They decide this in a way you might guess: with pathways built from past oxytocin moments. Whatever triggered that sense of trust in your past turns it on more easily today. Early experience wires each gazelle to recognize the smell of its own herd. Your early oxytocin built core pathways that tell you when to expect support from others.

The oxytocin of childhood separates us mammals from reptiles. We mammals form attachments because we have more oxytocin. Reptiles only release oxytocin during the act of mating (which lasts a few seconds) and while laying eggs. We mammals are born into a surge of oxytocin because the chemical triggers labor and lactation in mothers. More oxytocin is triggered when a mother cuddles or licks her baby. Neurons connect, which helps oxytocin flow faster in similar situations. A reptile doesn't let down its guard near fellow reptiles. A lizard doesn't seek support from other lizards. Mammals do, because they have more oxytocin.

You may have heard that hugging stimulates oxytocin. But if you hug someone you don't like, it doesn't really feel good. It doesn't meet your need for social support. It doesn't help you let down your guard. Trust is what our mammal brain is looking for. Trust comes before touch.

This is easy to see in the animal world. **Baboons make careful decisions about who grooms their fur because a baboon who's close enough to touch you is close enough to kill you.** The decisions are made with oxytocin pathways built from past experience.

New oxytocin pathways can build, but it takes a lot of repetition. Small oxytocin moments over time can build a pathway that makes it easier to trust a new individual. We want the good feeling of oxytocin all the time, so it's important to know that it is not meant to flow all the time. If it did, you would trust people you shouldn't trust. That would not promote survival. **Our brain is designed to save the oxytocin for real trust, not to release it constantly for no reason. This is why we seek moments of social trust so eagerly.**

Any oxytocin you manage to stimulate is quickly metabolized by your body. The good feeling passes, and you have to find another social-trust moment to enjoy more. This is why people are always searching for bonding opportunities.

Oxytocin is often misunderstood because social bonds are idealized. We think animals have glorious togetherness, so we feel like we're missing something. It's important to know the full story. Herd animals are not focused on "the greater good" the way it seems. They hide behind others to avoid being eaten. They push toward the center of the herd where it's safer. As they weaken with age, they lose these pushing wars, and end up around the edges where the risk of being picked off is higher. They have already reproduced by then, so the species survives.

A baboon expects something in return when it grooms another baboon's fur. A reciprocal grooming is nice, but there are other forms of payback in the baboon world. Reproductive opportunity is a big one. That could be sex when mating season arrives, or babysitting that helps your offspring survive. Another form of payback is protection when you are threatened. That could be a weaker mammal grooming a stronger individual to get protection from predators, or a stronger mammal grooming a weaker one to get support when a rival challenges their dominance.

Reciprocity is the name of the game in the mammal world. It's easy to see this in humans, though it's not polite to say so. People often pretend they are giving without expectations, but they are bitter when their expectations are disappointed. Our big brains can create abstract expectations, like the idea that you are good to the world so the world should be good to you. Then you get mad at the world when it falls short of your expectations. You can end up mad a lot. You are better off noticing the expectations you have.

It's helpful to know that baboons don't always get the reciprocation they expect. When this happens, they search for a new grooming partner. It's hard to believe that monkeys keep score, but field research shows that they do. The bad feeling of cortisol helps them do it, as we'll see on Day 6.

It's hard to keep oxytocin flowing, even for animals. Baboons spread out when they're safe from predators because that helps them avoid conflict in their search for food. Once they smell a predator, they forget their differences and gather to defend against it. **Mammals unite in the face of common enemies.** The only mammals who don't form groups are the ones with no predators: tigers and orangutans. (You may be thinking that lions have no predators, but hyenas steal their food when they're alone.)

It's easy to see how humans unite in the face of common enemies. **Whether a family, a company, or a country, people unite when they see a common threat.** You can observe this throughout human history and throughout your own day. Each time you talk to a group of people, notice the common enemy they focus on. You will see how often they call attention to their "enemy" to feel united and enjoy oxytocin.

Our verbal brain struggles to make sense of oxytocin's ups and downs. We strive to attach words to these primal feelings. We often call it "love." When others fail to meet your expectations, you may call it "betrayal." Your verbal brain doesn't know how you create these feelings, so it takes them as facts about the external world. When you know how you produce them internally, you have power over them.

When you feel accepted, an oxytocin circuit is triggering that feeling. You expect support because you got it in that context before. **Tiny cues are enough to trigger the feeling that you're safely with your herd.** And without those tiny cues, you may have a vague sense of threat without knowing why. The feeling that you belong or don't belong comes from internal pathways even though we imagine it as fact.

Idealized notions about social bonds often get in the way of oxytocin. If you expect support in specific ways and don't get it, you deprive yourself of oxytocin. Unrealistic expectations are common because our brains are wired in youth, when support comes without reciprocating, or with reciprocation designed to please a parent. That doesn't work in the adult world, but it feels right because the pathway is there. It helps to know that children reciprocate in a significant way: by promoting the survival of their parents' genes. It sounds crude to say that, but it explains why parents invest so much in their kids.

Parents cannot live forever, so mammals survive by transferring their attachment from parents to peers. Oxytocin helps them do that. Past experience with social trust helps a mammal find new opportunities for social trust. Each positive interaction helps new circuits build. There are plenty of disappointments along the way, of course. We'll explore the cortisol of disappointed trust on Day 6.

Childhood oxytocin circuits are never a perfect guide to adult social life. Sometimes they're just plain wrong. They can seduce you into trusting when it's not really safe, or scare you away from people who really do support you. Social trust is hard for everyone. Those who got less support from parents are challenged to build positive expectations about social support, while those who got a lot of support are challenged to build realistic expectations about adult life.

Fortunately, you can build new oxytocin circuits by feeding your brain new experiences, repeatedly. It takes time, alas, which is why people are so tempted by fast, easy oxytocin. Our world is full of fast but unsustainable paths to social support.

To complicate life further, our brain is always focused on the un-met need, so when your physical needs are met, social needs seem urgent. This is why small disappointments in your quest for oxytocin can preoccupy you. To make matters worse, your brain habituates to the social bonds you have, so it takes new social trust to really get your oxytocin going. If you have a great party and a good time is had by all, the oxytocin is soon over and you long for more. Managing an oxytocin-seeking brain is a challenge that comes with the gift of life.

MAKE IT HAPPEN

The urge for oxytocin is a huge motivator in our lives. These exercises help you recognize the quest for oxytocin all around you.

o **Notice things people do in order to belong to a group and avoid feeling isolated.**

_____

_____

o Identify the "common enemy" that unites different groups of people that you know.

_____

_____

_____

o Notice how people seek protection and support from others, and what they offer in exchange.

_____

_____

_____

Day 4

THE PRIDE OF SEROTONIN

Today you will learn:
o **how social recognition triggers serotonin**
o **why animals care about social importance**
o **why it's never enough**

We hear a lot about serotonin in the context of anti-depressants, but we don't hear much about its natural job. Serotonin creates a good feeling when a mammal gains a position of strength. It's not aggression; it's the nice calm feeling that you are strong enough to meet your needs in a world of social rivals.

It's easy to see that people enjoy being in a dominant position, though it's considered "not nice" to feel this way. That's why the urge for serotonin is easy to see in others, but we hate to acknowledge it in ourselves. To make life harder still, serotonin is quickly metabolized, so even when you gain an advantage, the good feeling is soon over. You have to see yourself in a position of strength again and again to keep feeling it. This is frustrating, so unsustainable strategies are tempting. A realistic understanding of your brain can help you avoid these temptations. First, let's see how it works in animals.

Monkeys seek a position of strength because their survival depends on it. A monkey is likely to get bitten if it grabs food that a bigger troop mate had its eye on. To avoid starving, a monkey has to find food that is not near a bigger monkey. To keep its genes alive, it has to find mating opportunity that is not near a bigger monkey. **Natural selection built a brain that constantly compares itself to others and rewards you with serotonin when you see that you're in the one-up position.** The good feeling is not meant to flow all the time for no reason. A monkey would not survive if it thought it was stronger when it wasn't.

The mammal brain defines "one-up" in simple ways. It doesn't create abstractions about the world at large. It just compares itself to the individual next to it in that moment. These comparisons rest on neural pathways built from past serotonin experience. Young monkeys spend a lot of time wrestling with others. We call it "play," but it trains a little monkey to judge its own strength. **When it's overpowered, its brain**

releases cortisol. When it prevails, serotonin is released and it feels good. Without conscious thought, a monkey makes accurate assessments of when to assert and when to submit. Monkeys test their strength against others a lot because serotonin rewards them when they win.

We have inherited the brain that makes social comparisons and longs for the one-up position. The urge for social comparison is more primal than food and sex in the sense that it always comes first. This is why people drive themselves crazy over small social differences when their lives are actually safer and more comfortable than anything in human history. And it's why people may strive for the position of strength in ways that may hurt them in the long run.

There is no easy solution to the serotonin quest. If you always see yourself as the big monkey who can grab the dominant position, you end up with a lot of conflict with other dominance-seeking monkeys. If you always see yourself as the weaker monkey, you avoid conflict but deprive yourself of serotonin. However you compare yourself, you rely on old circuits without noticing them. You think you're just seeing the facts so you have no other choice.

In the modern world, we invest a lot of energy in the quest for serotonin because less energy is used to meet physical needs. Our brain focuses on the un-met need, so your social standing can take on life-or-death importance without conscious intent.

We often jump to the conclusion that others have the one-up position handed to them, and they float through life on an effortless cloud of serotonin. It's easy to conclude that you're shortchanged or missing out. A deeper look at the serotonin facts of life will help you avoid these corrosive presumptions.

Social hierarchies are observed in most animal herds and packs and troops. Mammals strive to raise their status in the group because brains that did that made more surviving copies of their genes. Animals don't think about genes or social hierarchies in a cognitive way, of course. They just look for ways to feel good and avoid feeling bad. The mammal brain rewards you with the good feeling of serotonin when you raise your status. This is why humans strive so hard to raise their status even when their cognitive mind insists they don't care. Be it economic status, moral superiority, or physical skills, serotonin makes you feel good when you think you're on top.

Managing a serotonin-seeking brain is a challenge for everyone. When you're young, you dream of a position of importance. Once you achieve something, you soon habituate, and dream of the next level. You see a world full of rivals who want to steal your position, so it seems like you can never rest.

Imagine a young actor who dreams of a leading role. Once they get it, they dream of winning an award. Eventually, they become a star, but instead of enjoying it, they worry about losing their position to new actors coming along. The tabloids are proof that status doesn't make you happy. But people keep believing that the next rung on the ladder will make them feel good because past serotonin moments wired in the expectation.

You have probably been told that "our society" is to blame for this mindset. You have probably been taught to blame it on males, or "the rich," or another social group. Blame is a natural response to our serotonin frustrations. But when you blame externals, you feel powerless. You have power when you understand your internal thought loops.

It feels like the world is judging you until you understand your mammalian impulses. Then you see that you are doing a lot of judging yourself. You cannot control the world but you have some control over your own brain. You can find sustainable ways to satisfy your natural urge for serotonin. A simple way to do it is commonly known as "pride." Taking pride in your next step will spark a bit of serotonin, and when it's gone, you can take pride in the step after that. It takes a lot of effort to do things you're proud of, and serotonin rewards you for doing it.

Humans have struggled with the urge for social dominance since time began. No one wants a world where everyone tries to dominate everyone else, so humans train their children to manage this impulse.  But it's complicated, because we're tempted to manage it in others and deny it in ourselves. Your verbal brain finds reasons why you deserve the one-up position. You are just getting even with "them." You think you're just trying to survive, because your inner mammal makes you feel like you will die if you're in the one-down position. It's hard to believe that this impulse is natural, so let's look at more animal examples.

A female monkey that's stronger will get more food and thus make richer milk and stronger babies. Strength also helps her protect her offspring from predators. One surprising kind of predator is her female troop mate. Sometimes they kidnap the babies of weaker females. The baby dies of dehydration after a few hours without milk, and the mother cannot just grab it back because injury is likely when the predatory female resists. **You may find it hard to accept such nastiness among cute, furry creatures. It conflicts with the romanticized image of animals that has become popular. But the facts help us understand the job our brain evolved to do.**

More facts are necessary to get the full picture. Little monkeys get special treatment as long as they have *juvenile markings*, like the white tuft of fur that little chimpanzees have. Once juvenile markings fade, a little monkey has to compete for food with the rest of the troop. When a group of monkeys finds food, the strongest individual dominates the prime spot in front of it, and the other monkeys array themselves in order of relative strength. A little monkey must know its place to avoid getting bitten. It may end up at the fringes, where it gets less food and more exposure to predators. It is highly motivated to build its strength and get a better spot. Serotonin rewards it each time it asserts and prevails.

Puberty intensifies social rivalry. You may think sex comes easily to animals, but there is no free love in nature. Animals work hard for any reproductive opportunity they get. If they fail, their genes are wiped off the face of the earth. This is why the mammal brain responds with life-or-death chemistry to small social dramas. It's why one-up moments feel so good, and one-down moments feel so devastating.

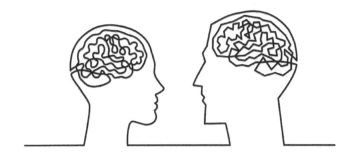

Managing the urge for serotonin is a skill we start learning in youth. If you grab another child's toy, you learn from the immediate consequences, whatever they may be. Every child wants the serotonin of self-assertion, but also the oxytocin of social acceptance and the dopamine of something new. There is no simple way to get this, so we just repeat things that worked before. If you got respect when you hit a home run, you learned to expect good feelings from similar activities. If you got respect by getting angry, your brain wired itself to seek the good feeling by getting angry. The neurons active in your early serotonin moments built connections that help you seek it today.

The verbal brain explains these impulses in ways that put you in the one-up position. You see yourself as a good person who is just trying to survive in a world of jerks. Moral superiority feels good for a moment, but it's not sustainable. Once the serotonin is metabolized, you feel one-down, so you have to feel morally superior again. No one is an objective judge of their social world. When you assert yourself, it seems only fair, but when a rival asserts, it seems dangerous and evil. To keep enjoying moral superiority, you have to keep seeing others as evil. It's no way to happiness.

Caring about others is often touted as the way to happiness. People say they only care for others and don't want anything for themselves. Superior virtue brings a moment of serotonin, but it doesn't last. **Your inner mammal feels squashed when you say that others matter and you don't.** You feel wrongly deprived. It's not a sustainable strategy.

Being "big" would not bring you endless serotonin either. It would not free you from the ups and downs of a serotonin-seeking brain. You are better off knowing how to manage your brain. You can have that now without waiting to be "big."

We have to keep reminding ourselves that our social-comparison thoughts are not real facts about the world. They are chemicals triggered by old neural pathways. You can build new pathways to serotonin by taking pride in your next step. You can feel one-up without putting others down. You only get a small squirt of serotonin from that, but then you can step with pride again and trigger more.

It's easy to see that people yearn for social importance despite its taboo-ness. Your inner mammal dwells on the social importance of others. It thinks they are putting you down and sees that as a threat. When you know how you create these feelings, you can just relax.

MAKE IT HAPPEN

Complete these exercises to understand the serotonin impulse in the world around you.

o **Notice things people do to feel strong or important in the eyes of others.**

_____

_____

_____

o **Notice how often people compare themselves to others, and how they differ in their basis of comparison.**

_____

_____

_____

o **Notice the way people fear losing their source of strength or pride.**

_____

Day 5

THE CHALLENGE OF ENDORPHIN

Today you will learn:
o **why pain triggers endorphin**
o **why we're not meant to seek endorphin**
o **a safe way to stimulate it**

Many people know endorphin from "runner's high." It was the first happy chemical to get attention, so the word "endorphins" is often used to mean happy chemicals in general. In truth, endorphin is less important than the other chemicals because it's for emergencies only.

Endorphin is triggered by physical pain. It's the body's natural opioid, and masks pain with a good feeling for a few minutes. That enables an injured creature to run for its life. When a gazelle's flesh is ripped open by a lion, endorphin masks pain long enough for the gazelle to take action to save itself. In twenty minutes, the endorphin stops, and the gazelle will feel pain if it has survived. **Pain promotes survival by telling you that an injury needs protecting.**

If a cave man fell and broke his leg, endorphin would give him a few minutes to seek help. You've had the endorphin experience if you've ever fallen and said you were fine, only to feel serious pain twenty minutes later. Pain triggers endorphin, which creates a euphoria that masks pain.

Endorphin evolved to promote survival, not to make you happy. We are not meant to inflict pain on ourselves to get endorphin because that would not promote survival. **We are NOT meant to seek endorphin.** We are meant to seek the other happy chemicals, but save endorphin for emergencies.

Yet people do seek it, so it's useful to know more. Like the other happy chemicals, neurons connect when endorphin flows, so we get wired to expect a good feeling from behaviors that trigger it. And **because our brain habituates, it takes more and more pain to stimulate it.** This is a bad loop. A simple example is stepping into a hot tub. It feels great for the first few minutes because of endorphin, but you soon habituate and it stops feeling good. Hotter water would trigger more endorphin, but that would be dangerous and stupid. When you understand your natural impulses, you can manage them better.

Hot pepper is another example. One squirt of pepper sauce triggers endorphin if you're not used to it, but soon it takes two or three squirts. You would hurt your insides if you chased endorphin in that way, and you wouldn't even know why you're doing it. Your verbal brain could say you have gourmet palette, but it's still not sustainable.

Exercise is a well-known example of chasing endorphin. You get a tiny drip of endorphin every

time you get off the couch, but you only get a "high" if you exercise to the point of pain. More pain is always needed, so this is not a sustainable path to happiness. Yet this path has become popular, so we need to understand it.

If you trigger your endorphin in a moment when you're feeling bad, your brain learns that endorphin can relieve bad feelings. The next time you feel bad, you think of repeating the endorphin-triggering behavior because the pathway is there. You haven't fixed the underlying cause of the bad feeling, of course, so it's not a sustainable solution. It's just a distraction.

Distraction is popular because it works. It would not work if you were chased by a lion, but if your bad feeling is caused by imagining a lion, distraction works. We humans imagine threats a lot. Our cortex tries to protect us from threats by anticipating them, but we end up anticipating a lot of threats. Distraction interrupts distressing thoughts, and that relieves the bad feeling. Exercise can distract you from bad thoughts. But if you exercise to the point of pain whenever you have bad thoughts, you can end up hurting yourself. It takes more and more pain to keep triggering endorphin, so you can end up with permanent injury.

We do not need endorphin. We need dopamine, serotonin, and oxytocin, but chasing endorphin does not help you get them. It is not the key to happiness. But it's nice to know **a safe way to trigger endorphin: laughing.** Laughter triggers deep abdominal muscles that don't usually get a workout. It's only a small endorphin release, but you can get more by laughing more. Real laughs are the way to activate these muscles, so do what it takes to expand the laughter in your life.

You may say there's not much to laugh about, but if you can't laugh until the world is perfect, you deprive yourself of endorphin. Instead, here are some simple ways to give yourself the endorphin of laughter.

First, don't suppress your laughs. Many people squelch their laughter because they think it looks bad. If you learned to squelch at a young age, you do it so automatically that you don't even notice. Whoever taught you not to laugh was misinformed. Laughter is a sustainable path to endorphin. You can learn to  notice your squelching habit and redirect it. You can give yourself permission to laugh and enjoy the rewards.

Second, prioritize your own sense of humor. You may miss out on content that makes you laugh because you defer to other people's entertainment choices. Instead, you can make space for what you think is funny. You can find ways to bond with friends and family without sacrificing your endorphin.

Finally, plan. That may seem strange, but it takes time to find things that make you laugh. I have to search through long lists of comedy that I don't like before I find things I like. I search when I'm in a good mood so I'm ready with lists of funny stuff on a bad day. You can stock your pantry with healthy humor the way you stock up on healthy snacks.

It may seem like others are high on endorphin all the time, but they are not. This chemical evolved for emergencies. We are not meant to chase it, so it is not discussed further in this book.

MAKE IT HAPPEN

Complete these exercises to understand the urge for endorphin in yourself and others.

o **Think of a time when you injured yourself but didn't feel it for a while. Ask others if they've noticed this.**

_____

_____

_____

o Think of ways that people inflict pain on themselves to get endorphin. Find the habit loop in their thoughts and actions.

_____

_____

_____

o List ways that you can add laughter to your life.

_____

_____

_____

Day 6

THE PAIN OF CORTISOL

Today you will learn:

o **how cortisol makes you feel like your survival is threatened**

o **why we have false alarms**

o **why we love whatever relieves cortisol**

Cortisol is nature's emergency broadcast system. It creates the feeling that something horrible is happening. It motivates you to do what it takes to make it stop, and prepares your whole body for action. But you don't always know how to make it stop because the mammal brain can't tell you in words why it's releasing cortisol. No wonder it's called the "stress chemical."

A gazelle's cortisol surges when it smells a predator, and it runs because that stops the cortisol.

Conscious thought is not needed for cortisol to do its job. Your cortisol works without conscious thought too. You urgently want it to stop, but it's hard to know why because you're not consciously thinking that a predator is about to eat you. Bad feelings are easier to manage when you know how you create them. Neurons connect when cortisol flows, so you're wired to turn it on fast when you see something linked to your cortisol past. The alarm bells you have were built by your own past experience. Today, you'll learn about your natural sense of alarm so it's easier to find the "off" switch.

Cortisol is designed to get your attention. A gazelle would rather keep eating when it smells a predator, but it runs because cortisol feels so bad. Hunger triggers cortisol too, so a gazelle only runs when predator cues trigger even more cortisol. It decides that with neural pathways built from its own past experience. It is not consciously trying to save its life because its brain does not support abstractions like life or death. It is just trying to feel good by making a bad feeling stop. But how does it know what to do? Let's look deeper.

Cortisol is triggered by pain. The jaws of a predator trigger lots of cortisol. But if you had to get bitten before you decided to run, few critters would survive. Cortisol promotes survival by giving advance warning. It does this in a fascinating way. Imagine you're a lizard being eaten by an eagle. Your tail is in its beak, but you manage to wriggle out and save your life. The pain of the eagle's beak in your flesh triggered cortisol. That built connections between all the neurons active at that moment. This includes the sudden darkness you experienced when the eagle swooped in. The next time a sudden darkness happens, you run for your life. Reptiles have very few extra neurons to build new circuits, but the ones they have are for just this purpose.

We humans have a lot of extra neurons available to build advance warning circuits. You don't have to touch a hot stove twice because the pain of the first touch builds a big cortisol pathway. The next time you see a hot stove, cortisol turns on in time to warn you to pull your hand back. It happens so fast that you don't consciously notice. Our Stone-Age ancestors grew up  around fires, and cortisol wired them to do what it takes to avoid pain. Today, we don't want our children to learn from pain, but we need to understand the alarm system we've inherited.

We anticipate pain a lot because that's our brain's survival strategy. No conscious thought is needed for us to anticipate pain and rush to escape it. Even when your verbal brain says "it doesn't bother me," or you don't notice that you're feeling threatened, your cortisol circuits can turn on the feeling that something is urgently wrong. You feel like you have to make it stop fast to avoid disaster. But how?

With whatever made it stop in your past. Food stops the bad feeling of hunger, so the animal brain seeks food when low blood sugar triggers cortisol. Fire stops the bad feeling of cold, so our ancestors looked for firewood. They didn't wait until they were hungry or cold. They anticipated future threats and acted in advance to relieve them, thanks to cortisol.

But much of the time, it's not so clear what triggered your bad feeling, or what will make it stop. For example, imagine that your boss or your spouse says "we need to talk." A sense of doom fills your body, even though you don't consciously expect physical pain. You assume there's a real threat because you can't believe an old pathway would cause this strong feeling. Let's look even deeper at why we anticipate pain.

A lion needs a full tank of energy in order to prevail in a chase. So instead of waiting until it's starving to hunt, cortisol sounds the alarm in advance. Without conscious intent, a lion anticipates future hunger in  time to relieve it. You have probably gone to the refrigerator before you were actually hungry! Your brain learned that food can relieve cortisol, so when you're feeling bad, you give that a try.

The mammal brain anticipates social pain as well as physical pain. Social pain is any threat to your ability to meet a social need. In the state of nature, social pain and physical pain are connected because getting separated from the group brings the risk of predator attack. If a gazelle waited until it was isolated to start feeling threatened, it would not survive, so cortisol motivates it to anticipate the threat and stay close. Mammals scan constantly for the whereabouts of their troop mates in order to feel safe. It's easy to see why your brain releases cortisol when your quest to meet social needs hits a snag.

Any social pain in your past wired you to turn on the cortisol when you see a similar situation today. A gazelle is not born fearing social isolation, but experience soon wires it in. When a young gazelle wanders away from mother's milk, it soon gets hungry, so its brain links separation to the pain of hunger. The mother panics when it wanders off, and the child mirrors the mother's panic when they reunite. Finally, Mom bites the child to reinforce the lesson. The pain of the bite amplifies the connection between separation and pain. **A young gazelle is soon wired to run when the herd runs without conscious awareness of what it is running from.**

A different kind of social pain is the one-down feeling. Your brain releases cortisol when you see that you're in a one-down position because this promotes survival in the state of nature. Imagine you're a little monkey and you start wrestling with a pal. They are stronger than you expect and they quickly dominate you. **Cortisol warns you to back off before you get hurt.** Neurons connect, and wire you to feel bad faster when you're dominated. This response could save your life some day when you cross paths with a stronger troop mate. Cortisol wires us to withdraw to avoid conflict. We'd rather not withdraw, so it takes a bad feeling to motivate that.

We all have cortisol circuits telling us when to feel threatened and how to escape the perceived threat. We all have a history of cortisol because we're born with needs that we're helpless to meet. Your verbal brain struggles to explain your threatened feelings. It may dismiss them as "irrational" and try to ignore them. But they don't go away, so you are better off knowing why your brain trusts its own alarm system.

Cortisol promotes survival by alerting you to important information. A gazelle gathers information before it runs so it doesn't run in the wrong direction. When your cortisol turns on, you scan for information about the threat. Cortisol is nature's danger radar (with the help of the chemical *adrenaline*.) You look for threat signals without conscious intent because the electricity in your brain flows so effortlessly into pathways built up by your past cortisol.

It's hard to solve problems while your cortisol is surging because you focus on the drawbacks of possible solutions. It helps to know that cortisol has a half life of twenty minutes. That means your body eliminates half of it in that time, and half of what remains in the next twenty minutes. Most of it is gone in an hour, unless you trigger more. But we do trigger more much of the time because we're so good at finding more evidence of threat. Our cortex tries to help with its extra-large information processing capacity. When you find mpreore threat signals, you release more cortisol, and thus scan for more threat signals. A cortisol spiral can result. Now what?

Stop and do something you like for twenty to forty minutes, to distract your brain from threat-seeking. If you keep trying to solve the problem while your cortisol is surging, you'll feel as desperate as a gazelle who sees no escape route. Things will look different when most of the cortisol is gone. This does not work in real emergencies, but you can learn to stop seeing old cortisol responses as real emergencies.

It's hard to do nothing when cortisol is screaming "do something!" This is why unhealthy distractions are popular. They make it easier to shift from a bad feeling to a good feeling. But you can find healthy distractions with a bit of advance planning. First, list things you enjoy. This is not the time to take on "good-for-you" activities. Be honest with yourself about your likes, but broaden your list with new possibilities. Good prospects are activities that engage mind and body together (like cooking, gardening, playing an instrument, arts and crafts), because they're so good at distracting from negative thoughts. Now prepare a way to engage in these activities for twenty to forty minutes during cortisol moments. That could mean buying supplies, creating a travel kit, or just giving yourself permission to do that thing you always wanted to do. It also means setting a timer for twenty to forty minutes so you put down the activity and return to tackling the problem.

Humans have always struggled to understand their cortisol. It helps to know that **disappointment triggers it**. If you don't get the pony you wanted for Christmas, you don't consciously think your survival is threatened, but cortisol makes it feel that way. To see why, imagine you're a hungry lion and the gazelle you are chasing gets away. Cortisol surges and motivates you to stop the chase. You hate to stop because you're so close and so hungry. It takes a very bad feeling to override the expectation of a reward. **The bad feeling promotes survival because you'd starve to death if you kept chasing gazelles that got away. You have to know when to give up in order to have energy left for better prospects.** The cortisol of disappointment helps us make good decisions about where to invest our energy. Neurons connect and we learn to anticipate disappointment in similar future settings. Once cortisol flows into the pathway, it feels like a real threat.

Our ancestors survived by trusting their cortisol. Their children were not eaten by predators because they anticipated threats and took precautions. Cortisol helps you anticipate threats so you act in time to prevent them. But you don't notice your success because your big brain quickly scans for the next potential threat. It all feels less threatening when you understand your cortisol.

MAKE IT HAPPEN

Complete these exercises to understand the power of cortisol in your daily life.

o **Notice someone feeling bad and figure out what pain they are anticipating.**

_____

_____

o **When you feel bad, notice how your verbal brain tries to explain and relieve it.**

_____

_____

_____

o **When you feel bad, notice the way you look for evidence of threat, and perhaps trigger more threatened feelings.**

_____

_____

_____

Day 7

YOUR DOPAMINE PAST

Today you will:
○ **discover your old dopamine pathways**
○ **recognize the habits you have for stimulating dopamine**
○ **identify the early experience that built your old dopamine pathways**

Dopamine tells you "I can get it!" It feels great, but you would not benefit from feeling it every minute. You'd end up chasing things that don't serve you in the long run. Our brain is designed to make careful decisions about when to release it, but it relies on old dopamine pathways to do that. They are not perfect guides to today's reality, so it's good to know that you can adjust your old pathways once you learn to notice them. It takes work, however, and you won't do the work until you recognize their power.

The electricity in your brain flows like water in a storm, finding the paths of least resistance. The world floods your brain with more detail than you can process, so you make sense of things by letting electricity flow into pathways created by past experience. When you see something linked to a past dopamine experience, electricity zips to the "on" switch of your dopamine. This is how we get excited without knowing why.

The challenge of understanding your dopamine is complicated by the word "rewards." You may have heard that you should focus on a higher purpose instead of "rewards." But your brain defines "higher purpose" with pathways built from your dopamine past. It focuses on social rewards when your physical needs are met. Our energy is limited so our brain only spends it when it expects a return, however your circuits define that.

Early experience is what builds the superhighways of your brain because a young brain has a lot of *myelin*. This chemical coats a neuron the way insulation coats a wire, helping electricity to flow at super speeds. Your myelinated neurons are so efficient that they activate without effort. When you let electricity flow into a pathway you myelinated in youth, things make sense instantly. We have a lot of myelin before age eight and during puberty, so your repeated experiences in those years built the core neural networks that you have today.

You don't have to remember these experiences for them to shape your responses. You feel like you are just seeing the facts. To understand the power of neural pathways, imagine that your neighbor comes home with a new car. You never saw this model before, but once you see it in their driveway, you

notice it everywhere. How is that possible? Because seeing it in their driveway connected that cluster of neurons, so your electricity flows there effortlessly.

Before you connected these neurons, the car did not fit a pattern already stored in your brain. So you saw it as isolated details rather than a meaningful whole. Electricity doesn't flow easily along undeveloped neurons, and that's why it's hard to interpret new inputs. You can see something new if you invest the energy necessary to push electricity through small pipes, and thus connect it to your existing knowledge. Otherwise, the flow just stops and you lose awareness of the information.

You wired in your neighbor's car without conscious effort because repetition is what it takes. If you had strong feelings about the car, either positive or negative, the circuit would have built even faster. If you saw the car when you were young, the pathway would be even bigger. **Experience develops neurons in a way that creates meaning.**

You don't consciously know how you tell the difference between one car and another. A toddler tells the difference between a dog and a cat without consciously knowing how. And in the same way, you tell the difference between what is good for you and what is bad for you. It's just electricity flowing into a pathway built from past experience.

You are not powerless over the electricity in your brain. You have some control over where it flows. It's hard to redirect it from a myelinated pathway into an undeveloped neuron, yet you succeed at doing it many times a day.

Doing a jigsaw puzzle is a simple example. You see a hole of a certain shape, and you scan for a piece that matches. Dopamine rewards you when you find a match. Then you do it again, holding a shape in your mind and scanning for a match. It takes conscious effort to hold these shapes in your mind. Dopamine

rewards each success, which is why people do puzzles.

You do the same basic thing when you look for a new job or a new lover. You activate an image of what you need, and then scan the world for a match. The difference between finding a puzzle piece and finding work or love is that the shape of a puzzle piece is arbitrary, but the shape of the job or partner you seek is a cluster of expectations about meeting your needs. These expectations are built from your accumulated experience with rewards and pain.

Sometimes we seek rewards that hurt us in the long run. We don't know why because we're not aware of the stored patterns that guide our search. You would make different choices if you wired in a new pattern. And you can!

Step One is noticing your old pattern. Step Two is designing an alternative path to your dopamine. Step Three is repeating the alternative until a new pathway builds. You'll complete Steps Two and Three on Day 11, so let's start with discovering your old paths to dopamine.

Sometimes it's easier to see these patterns in others. When I was a kid, my mother always put an orange in my Christmas stocking. I couldn't understand why she would grab something from the refrigerator to stuff my stocking. After she died, I learned that oranges were a huge luxury when she was young. If she got one for Christmas, it would have triggered her dopamine. So her brain saw it as a treat, while my brain saw it as something taken for granted. Each brain sees the world through the lens of its own pathways.

To find your own dopamine pathways, it helps to know that **dopamine's core job is prediction.** Our brain constantly makes predictions in order to survive, and dopamine rewards you when they're correct. Our ancestors predicted where water could be found and where a hunted animal might run. Bad predictions were a survival threat, so you were highly motivated to improve your predictions. Today, **we make predictions about the weather, sports, politics, the stock market, and even the lottery, and we enjoy a bit of dopamine when we're right.**

You predict where a parking spot might be found in order to get your errands done. A chess player is always predicting which move will work. A wine enthusiast is always predicting which bottle will be good. A job seeker is always predicting which job opening will reward their efforts. The joy of dopamine rests on making correct predictions.

Each correct prediction builds the pathway that guides you to make similar predictions in the future. It's hard to think of your joy in life as a quest for good predictions, so let's look at more examples.

Watching a movie or reading a novel is fun because you are always predicting how it will turn out. You keep searching for clues to piece the puzzle together, and dopamine spurts when you figure it out. That wires you to seek more good feelings from fiction. Mirror neurons enhance the good feeling as you watch characters enjoy dopamine, serotonin, or oxytocin. Your mind is distracted from threats while you're decoding fiction. No wonder it's popular.

Of course, you are not meeting   r e a l

needs when you consume fiction, but it can help clear your mind for better problem-solving later on. If later never comes, however, you miss out on the bigger dopamine spurts from taking action in real life.

Watching sports rests on the joy of predicting. You search your knowledge base for a pattern that fits this situation, and when your prediction is correct, dopamine! The mental activity distracts you from worry loops. You also get oxytocin if there's camaraderie, and serotonin from mirroring the pride of the athlete who scores. Neurons connect, so you expect more good feelings from the sport. Just thinking about your next sporting event gets your dopamine going.  Our brain did not evolve to care about a ball crossing a line, of course. It only cares if past experience wired you to expect good feelings from the activity.

Collecting is another popular path to dopamine. A collector is always scanning the world for new items that fit their collection. When they find one, dopamine! Collecting allows you to define your "needs" in a way that you can satisfy. You create a quest that you can succeed at. When the dopamine is over, you start a new quest.

Music is another dopamine-stimulating activity. It's hard to see it this way, but when you listen to music, you are searching for patterns and predicting their variations. Music stimulates your dopamine if it's familiar enough for you to predict correctly, but not so familiar that you can predict it without effort. Music relieves cortisol because your mind is too busy to ruminate on potential threats. It's a sustainable way to feel good, but you get much more dopamine from action to meet your needs.

Video games are a popular path to dopamine because they trigger the "I can get it" feeling over and over. Video games trigger dopamine because you predict which steps will approach the goal. There is always another step you can take for another reward. Oxytocin boosts the good feeling if you play with others, and serotonin boosts it when you win. Cortisol relief boosts the good feeling because the game shuts out unpleasant thoughts. Of course, you don't meet real needs or get real rewards when you play video games. And you don't use the energy that dopamine releases, which is why people feel wound up after playing.

Social media and smart phones are often blamed for dopamine habits. When you blame the device, you miss the chance to understand your pathways. These devices trigger dopamine because they help us meet our oxytocin and serotonin needs, as we'll see in the next two days. We can use our devices in healthy ways when we understand our own brain.

Sometimes people make bad predictions. An alcoholic predicts that they will be fine after another drink. A gambler predicts that they will win if they keep on gambling. Addiction rests on big past rewards, which built big expectations of more rewards. Past experience does not necessarily lead to good predictions about the world as it is. But we rely on it  anyway because the neurons activate so easily.

Fortunately, you can build new pathways if you feed your brain new information about the world, repeatedly. We often resist that because leaving an old path feels like a survival threat. You have to show your inner mammal that there are other paths to rewards. As you repeat the new path, electricity will flow and it will feel normal. You'll learn this on Day 11.

MAKE IT HAPPEN

Complete these exercises to recognize the power of your old dopamine pathways.

o **Notice when you feel excited about something. What reward in your past fit the same basic pattern?**

_____

_____

_____

o **Think about an activity that you like. Notice the way you feel the moment you start planning to do it.**

_____

_____

_____

o Think about things that made you happy as a child. What are you doing today that fits the same basic pattern?

_____

_____

_____

Day 8

YOUR OXYTOCIN PAST

Today, you will:

- notice patterns in your oxytocin-seeking efforts
- identify the early experience that built your oxytocin pathways
- recognize your urge to repeat behaviors that stimulated oxytocin in your past

We are all born helpless and needing support to survive. Oxytocin is released when you get support. Neurons connect and wire you to expect support in ways you got it before. These expectations don't make sense to your verbal brain much of the time, but you rely on them anyway. With courageous honesty, you can discover your old expectations about social support so you can build your power over them.

A newborn baby gets support by crying. It doesn't intend to cry. It cries in response to the cortisol that surges when its needs are not met. Crying is one of our only inborn skills, and it works: it brings support that meets a baby's needs. Gradually, a baby learns other ways of meeting needs and getting support. But it also learns that support is not always there. This does not mean bad parenting. Each new brain must learn that it's a separate person who cannot control others. Your skills grow with time, but you still have moments when you can't meet your needs, and your cortisol surges. You still want to scream for help. **Screaming has bad consequences in adult life, but the circuit that makes you want to scream is still there.**

We learn fancy language to talk about social support. This helps us get support, but it does not help us understand our own circuits. Let's look at some real oxytocin responses beneath the fancy talk. A simple example is a child whose parents smoke cigarettes with friends. The child's brain links the sounds of friendship to the smell of cigarettes. Today, they have a good feeling about smokers, though they don't know why.

Negative expectations build from experience too. For example, my mother was taking lamb out of the oven when she got the call that my grandmother died, and she never cooked lamb again. She did not consciously think she'd lose someone if she cooked lamb, of course, but big survival experiences build big pathways in the brain.

Your brain is always making decisions about social support with the pathways you happen to have. Old circuits are never a perfect guide, so we all need some adjustments. But we have to recognize the reality of our circuits before we can tailor them. We have to notice the patterns in our expectations about support in order to know that those patterns are not reality itself. Your myelinated pathways zoom in on some details of the world and ignore others. You keep making the same assumptions about the world until you notice your old pathways.

Let's look at the pathways built in adolescence because that experience is easier to remember than early childhood. And let's look at puberty in animals because it helps us see patterns that our verbal brain ignores. Monkeys and apes generally leave their parents at puberty because inbreeding would destroy a species. They don't consciously think that, but in most species, all the males leave or all the females leave. Natural selection built a brain that motivates you to build new social bonds in puberty. But an adolescent monkey is terrified when it leaves the support network it has. Isolation is a survival threat, so it rushes to find acceptance in a new group. Its oxytocin surges each time it gets support in a new place, and that wires it to expect good feelings there. A monkey can get rejected a lot before it finds acceptance, so it tends to stay with the troop that lets it in.

Sex triggers more oxytocin than just belonging, so monkeys are very motivated to find mating opportunity. Yet they are surprisingly particular. A young monkey must prove itself in various ways before it can mate. They have to build trust with repeated oxytocin moments. Thus, young monkeys are eager to do things that build trust.

Humans have similar impulses. **We seek new bonds in adolescence, and the urge for a partner motivates us to do things that build trust. Oxytocin surges when we find acceptance, and that wires us to repeat behaviors associated with that.**

Any moment of acceptance you felt as a teen built a pathway that told you "this is the way to go!" We don't think this consciously, so it's easier to see how it worked with our ancestors. They usually spent their lives with the same tribe or the same village, but if they moved, it was usually to get a mate. Once in a new group, they had to learn new faces, new skills, and a new way to get home in the dark. The myelin of puberty helped them wire in new paths to rewards. We all have more myelin in puberty, so your teen experiences are central to your reward-seeking pathways.

You may be embarrassed or even offended by the suggestion that you are running on a neural network built in adolescence. But if you look for patterns, you will see the match between your teen experiences and the way you seek social support today. It's comforting to know that everyone does this. We also wire in the fear we experience while transferring attachment from parents to peers. That fear is obscured by the adolescent urge for independence, but underneath that bravado are fears and disappointments that are often eerily similar to your present concerns.

Mirror neurons play a big role in our oxytocin

 learning. When you see another kid get atten-tion, mirror neurons spark the impulse to do what they do. The "popular" kid is imitated without

conscious intent. Horses mirror the lead horse in this way. They don't consciously choose a leader. They just imitate the horse who seems to know what it's doing.

When you see others get social support, it seems like they get it effortlessly all the time. You think they have an easy path to oxytocin because you don't see the sense of isolation that their mammal brain creates. You wonder what's wrong with your life. It helps to know that oxytocin is hard for everyone because it's quickly metabolized, so we have to keep finding more.

The selfish urge for support is obscured by the virtuous-sounding words we use to discuss it, like "altruism" and "empathy." Beneath abstract language, the mammal brain longs for protection. The expression "got your back" describes the feeling well. Subtle protection, like someone taking your side in a discussion, gives you a little drip of oxytocin. You get a big surge if someone literally rescues you from danger. That wires you to feel deeply bonded to the person, even if they are a bit shady.

The opposite is also true: if someone fails to protect you when you expect it, disappointment triggers cortisol. Neurons connect, and you see them as a threat without quite knowing why. We can rewire these circuits, but first we must recognize them.

It's harder to identify your circuits when you idealize social bonds. Getting real about the urge for protection helps you understand your strong reactions to ups and downs in social support. For example, when someone doesn't share your opinion, strong feelings may erupt because the mammal brain sees

social alliances as a matter of survival. When you don't know how you created these feelings, you conclude that the other person must actually be a threat.

Imagine that you make a new friend at school, and they ask you to cheat on exams with them. They insist that it's just "sharing," which all friends should do. You may fear losing your social support if you don't submit to their expectations. Cortisol is released, and wires you to fear losing friends in the future. You don't say this to yourself in words, but you may find yourself conforming to the expectations of others to relieve cortisol and sustain oxytocin.

Sometimes, you are the one with expectations. Others fail to meet them and you feel abandoned without knowing how you created this feeling. It's hard to notice your own expectations because they're just electricity flowing into pathways connected by past experience.

Everyone faces disappointment on the road to oxytocin. No child or teenager gets the support they hope for every minute. If they did, they would build unrealistic expectations that would be disappointed in their future. We all see the world through the lens of past disappointments.

Cortisol is released when you reach out for support and fail to get it. We avoid cortisol triggers, so we avoid reaching out and getting disappointed. **The result is inner conflict between the urge to get support and the fear of rejection.** The path to oxytocin is full of frustrating trade-offs.

In the past, this conflict was usually resolved by sticking with the herd. The world was so dangerous that you didn't dare face it alone. If you got frustrated with your herd, you didn't leave, because predators attack isolated individuals. Tensions within the tribe were relieved by focusing on common enemies. And **people did not expect the tribe to give them a child-like level of support in adulthood.**

Today, it's safer to live without the protection of a tribe, so people feel free to shop around for higher levels of support. But we still get disappointed due to unrealistic expectations. And we get disappointed because we look for protection from fellow mammals who are looking for protection themselves.

Sometimes we succeed at building mutual alliances. We get support by giving support. It's easier when we find allies who are offering the kind of support we desire, and desiring the kind of support we want to give. Such alliances meet our oxytocin needs with less cortisol. But it's hard to find such perfect reciprocity. It takes a lot of honesty about your own impulses and tolerance for disappointment while you search.

Indeed, mutual alliances are so hard to build that we often join alliances organized by others. These groups often hold together by accentuating common enemies, because that's what mammals do. This feels good in the short run because you get the social solidarity your inner mammal is looking for. But you have to stay focused on the common enemy to keep getting the rewards. You have to spend your energy protecting the group from its perceived threats, and in exchange you receive protection from their perceived threats. You can end up spending a lot of energy in ways that don't really meet your needs. It's not always a sustainable path to oxytocin.

Here's a simple example. Let's say you like art, so you join an art group. You find that the group spends a lot of time talking about enemies of art. They may not use the word "enemy," but they constantly bemoan adversaries who maliciously block your group's path to its deserved rewards. These enemies seem more and more threatening, so you stick with the group. It drains your energy without adding trust, or art, to your life.

Each person in a social alliance brings expectations from their own past experience. It's hard to sustain mutual trust when each person has different expectations that no one is aware of. **When you understand your own expectations about social support, you can see how you're filtering the world. Then you can design the pathway that best meets your needs. You can enjoy the world as it is instead of waiting for an ideal world.**

You can discover your own oxytocin circuits by exploring your early experience with social support. You will see how your sense of trust today fits the patterns of trust you experienced in the past. You will see how your disappointments today fit your past disappointments. On Day 12, you will learn to adjust these circuits.

It's hard to think about your early oxytocin because it triggers the vulnerability of youth. We avoid vulnerable thoughts because cortisol warns us off. But with practice, you will learn to separate your present reality from your early circuits. You will learn to see bad feelings as chemicals that you eliminate in an hour rather than evidence of real threat. You can build new expectations about social support instead of running on expectations created by accidents of experience.

MAKE IT HAPPEN

Complete these exercises to recognize the power of your old oxytocin pathways.

o **Notice a moment when you feel accepted or supported. What experience in your past fits the same basic pattern?**

_____

_____

_____

o Notice something you do because it helps you get support or acceptance. What similar behaviors can you remember in your early life?

_____

_____

_____

o Notice a moment when you fear being rejected, isolated or ignored. Look for early experiences that fit the same basic pattern.

_____

_____

_____

Day 9

YOUR SEROTONIN PAST

Today, you will:

o **identify the recognition you got in your early years**

o **notice how you seek social importance today, and find past patterns that fit**

o **notice your urge to repeat behaviors that made you special in your past**

No one likes to admit that they want to be special, but we've inherited a brain that seeks specialness as if your life depends on it. The desire for recognition is often condemned, so we tend to deny that we have these feelings. You can say you're less egoistical than others, which puts you in the one-up position while maintaining the illusion that you don't care about social position. The truth is, we all care about social importance despite our best intentions because serotonin makes it feel good. The serotonin is soon metabolized, so we have to find more specialness to keep feeling it. No wonder the world is full of "ego"!

When you fail to get the recognition you long for, your mammal brain thinks you're in the one-down position. Cortisol makes it feel like a survival threat, even when you're perfectly safe. Knowing this can free you from that sense of threat. Managing cortisol is tomorrow's subject. Today, we focus on the pathways that compare you to others and decide who's on top.

Whatever made you feel important in the past built pathways that tell you where to expect the good feeling today. **Those pathways motivate you to repeat behaviors that made you important in your past even if they're not good for you now.** Once you notice these patterns, you can offer your inner mammal more sustainable ways to feel one-up.

You may insist that others should change because they're the ones who fail to recognize your true worth. It's tempting to blame the world for undervaluing you. But we are not objective judges of the world around us. We see it through the lens of neural pathways designed to meet our needs. When you understand your natural longing for one-up moments, you will manage it better than others. (That was a shameless appeal to your one-up impulse!)

It's hard to get real about your serotonin pathways because old disappointments get stirred up. Your inner mammal is always doing the social-comparison dance. It zooms in on the strengths of others, and thus on your own weakness. You don't know how you're doing that, so it feels like others are putting you down.

Why do we put ourselves in the one-down position when we long for the one-up position?

There are so many reasons. Because mammals promote survival by being wary of stronger individuals. Because we got praised for taking the one-down position, so we learned that it's a way to be one-up. Because we mirror others who put themselves down. Soon, it feels so natural that you just flow there.

Let's see how this works in childhood when our core pathways are built. Kids seek the one-up position in any way that works. When they get power for a moment, serotonin makes it feel good and motivates them to repeat any behavior that worked. This early social drama is hard to remember with your verbal brain because you never thought it in words. It helps to remember little monkeys wrestling and learning about their relative strength.

When you were young, you measured yourself against others and drew conclusions without consciously intending to. Physical strength is less important for modern humans, and you can even hurt your social standing if you dwell on it. So you learn other skills for getting recognition. Your good and bad feelings paved pathways that tell you how you stack up against others today.

In the animal world, the ability to inflict pain is often the key to social power. Old movies remind us of a time when fist fights were a common way to assert yourself. Modern humans find alternatives, but many people alive today remember being hit or beaten as a child. Even schools used this "teaching tool." Fortunately, things have changed, but each generation must wire itself to redirect the natural urge for social dominance. If a toddler's tantrums get rewards, the child gets wired to expect rewards from tantrums. They may become like a little poodle who barks at big dogs. In the state of nature, little poodles build realistic expectations in order to avoid pain, but in the modern world of

overprotection, a person can reach adulthood without realistic self-management skills.

Your mammal brain is always judging your relative strength and looking for the next opportunity to be one-up. When you got recognition as a child, serotonin made the world look good, and stored the glory in your neurons. You repeated that behavior, but it didn't always work. Your one-up efforts failed sometimes. Cortisol made it feel awful and wired you to avoid that experience. But you can't avoid it because no one can be one-up all the time. You learned to fear that one-down feeling without knowing why. Your verbal brain tries to explain it, and learns words like "shame" and "loser."

Children often mirror their parents' feelings about social comparison. **It's easy to absorb their longing for recognition and their reaction to one-down moments.** It's easy to learn the way they explain these feelings. Even if you decide that you will not be like them, you will probably find surprising matches in your own patterns. The point is not to blame your parents but to know how we create our emotions.

The big human cortex keeps trying to help. It is good at finding "evidence" that you deserve the one-up position and are unfairly deprived of it. There are endless ways to do this, but the ways you hear repeatedly from others build pathways that make them seem true. You don't see how you create your one-down feelings with your natural quest for the one-up feeling.

As adults, we repackage the social-comparison impulses learned in childhood. You might decide that you're a better driver and sneer at other drivers on the road. You might sneer at people in the news and decide that you're a better human being. You might pride yourself on your access to good drugs. Maybe you tell yourself that you're a better son or daughter than your siblings. Maybe you think you are luckier than others, or holier, or smarter, or more compassionate. Each brain looks for a way to be special, and keeps on looking.

Many one-up habits are not sustainable. They hurt you in the long run, but you repeat them because they feel good right now. Snapping at your boss or partner is a common example. You feel one-up when you do it, and it happens so fast that you don't see it as a choice. To understand that choice, we need a closer look at childhood.

Children are often rewarded for bad behavior, so they get wired to repeat the bad behavior. For example, a child may get power or attention when they are oppositional. They repeat oppositional behaviors because serotonin built a pathway that expects it to feel good.

Another example is being weak and helpless. If a child gets a rush of support when they act incompetent, they feel special for a moment. When the good feeling passes, they can get more by letting others know how weak they are. No conscious intent is involved. The verbal brain finds good ways to explain your urge to repeat oppositional or helpless behaviors.

The human cortex has always struggled to explain the dominance-seeking impulses of the mammal brain it's attached to. This is why we have so many words for feelings about how we compare to others. We call it: pride, status, self-confidence, ego, glory, dominance, power, honor, dignity, self-worth, prestige, prominence, exclusivity, social importance, recognition, respect, approval, arrogance, assertiveness, self-aggrandizement, manipulativeness, competitiveness, fame, one-upmanship, self-righteousness, feeling superior, having class, saving face, and being influential, special, or a winner.

When you or your allies seek the one-up position, you find words that seem honorable and smart. When your rivals seek social dominance, you find words that make them seem unethical and stupid. There is no one right way to seek serotonin. It's a challenge for everyone.

To complicate things further, the brain habituates to any status you have, so you always feel like you have to do more. You have to be more brilliant or virtuous or oppositional or helpless, or whatever strategy you've learned. It's exhausting.

For this reason, people like to specialize. You strive to be really good at one thing, so you always have a reliable way to feel one-up. However, **you habituate to the applause you have, so you still keep feeling like you have to out-do yourself.** And you don't know how you created this treadmill. Your verbal brain finds a way to blame others.

Some people do the opposite of specializing. They have to be the best at everything. They want to be one-up all the time. They strive to be the belle of every ball and the center of every stage. They never stop chasing opportunities to be important. As soon as their serotonin fades, they feel one-down. They don't know how to manage the cortisol except with more one-upping. It's easy to critique this mindset in others, but it's useful to notice your own fear of the one-down position and the things you do to escape it.

You may feel foolish when you notice your own serotonin habits. It's understandable if you'd rather not think about it. So let's return to the serotonin-seeking of innocent children. Imagine two kids fighting over a cookie. Without adult intervention, the stronger child gets the cookie. Each brain learns from the experience, but the lesson learned depends on each child's other inputs. Let's explore the possibilities.

The kid who loses the cookie has a one-down moment, but that can lead in different directions:

- They might stop asserting because they expect to lose.
- They might rise to the challenge and strive to build strength to win next time. If they win, that could lead to self-confidence, but it could also lead to bullying and a "get-them-first" mindset.
- Or the child might seek third-party support. That can go different ways too. The child might learn to make articulate appeals for support, but they might

also learn to make shrill accusations in order to enjoy a moment of social dominance.

- The child might ignore their tormentor and seek support elsewhere, ending up with strong social skills and wide respect in their community.

Now let's shift to the perspective of the child who grabbed the cookie. That can go in many ways too.

- The child may learn to feel confident.
- The child may learn to rely excessively on physical strength and fail to build other strengths. Their bullying gets a bad reaction from others, but they don't understand why. They respond to the rejection with more bullying, and end up feeling bad a lot.
- The child notices the distress they cause in others and gives the cookie back. They might learn to be a good leader who combines strength with empathy, but they might just learn to pinpoint what they can get away with.

You may think cookie-grabbers enjoy effortless serotonin while cookie-losers suffer endlessly. But our emotional responses are complex webs built from a smorgasbord of experiences in our myelin years. You don't remember the little cookie conflicts of your past, but they shaped your adult feelings about rewards. You can find the patterns in your feelings about social power if you observe them carefully.

As you ponder these experiences, notice how the happy chemicals work together.

Dopamine and serotonin work together when you see a chance to "make it big." **Dopamine helps you take steps toward serotonin.**

Oxytocin and serotonin also work together. Oxytocin can motivate you to join a group, while serotonin motivates you to rise in the group. **Both chemicals are stimulated when you join efforts to raise the whole group.** No wonder this is so popular!

Sometimes, the happy chemicals conflict with each other instead of working together. **You could lose oxytocin when you take steps to "make it big," as your comrades fear being left behind. You could lose dopamine if your one-up fantasies are unrealistic so you never get closer.** Painful tradeoffs result. If you don't notice your old pathways, you just repeat the trade-offs you made before instead of reexamining them.

The serotonin urge is so frustrating that you may vow to stop comparing yourself to others. But you will probably keep comparing because you're a mammal. You might sneak it in by insisting that you are "too enlightened" to care about social comparison. That makes you superior, which distracts you from your one-down feelings. But soon you see "less enlightened" people get rewards that you don't have. A bad feeling turns on and your verbal brain tries to explain it. You easily flow into the thought that you are right and something is wrong with everyone else. Thus you enjoy one more unsustainable one-up moment.

You are better off recognizing your social-comparison circuits and your power to redirect them. You will stop feeling judged because you will know how your own mind does the judging. That makes it easier to just relax.

MAKE IT HAPPEN

Complete these exercises to understand your old serotonin pathways.

o **Notice a moment when you feel important or special. What experience in your past fit the same basic pattern?**

_____

_____

o Notice a moment when you feel one-down. What do you do to feel better? How did you do the same basic thing in your past?

_____

_____

_____

o Think of a moment of glory in your youth. How do your motivations today fit that general pattern?

_____

_____

_____

Day 10

YOUR CORTISOL PAST

Today, you will:
- ○ notice when you get upset and find the same basic patterns in your early experience
- ○ identify cortisol moments of your past and notice your urgent fear of such things today
- ○ observe things you do to relieve cortisol and how you did those things in your youth

Cortisol makes you feel like you will die if you don't act fast to make it stop. We've seen that disappointment triggers cortisol, which is why you feel so threatened when you don't get what you want. We've seen that the mammal brain cannot explain itself in words, so the verbal brain constructs "good reasons" for your threatened feelings. And we've also seen that a cortisol reliever feels like a lifesaver, so you are eager to repeat it. You can find new paths to relief when you understand your cortisol circuits.

How do you know what relieves a threat? A simple brain decides in simple ways, but a big brain makes it complicated. A gazelle feels relief when it escapes from the smell, sound, and sight of a predator, even though it still lives in a world full of predators. But a big brain knows that threats are still around somewhere. A big brain has trouble feeling safe because it's so good at constructing internal images of threats. This is why we're so eager for anything that brought relief before, even if it's not rational. **You're eager for anything that changed a bad feeling to a good feeling in your past.**

Here is a simple example. Imagine you're a teenager at a party and you want to talk to a special someone. Your cortisol surges and creates a head-to-toe terror when you think about chatting with the hottie. Someone offers you a drink in this moment and you accept for the first time. Then you approach the object of your desire and it works! They like you! You don't consciously think the drink made them like you, but your brain connects all the neurons active at that moment. The next time you fear talking to someone, the thought of alcohol pops into your head. You expect it to change the bad feeling to a good feeling because you've actually experienced that. Each drink strengthens the pathway. And each time you rely on this cortisol-relief strategy, you fail to build other effective self-soothers.

You may not remember the first moment that you learned your favorite relief strategy. But if you pull on the threads in your memory, you can probably unravel them. You will see patterns in your distress, and in your strategies for relieving it.

These patterns are hard to see with your logical brain because they're not logical. Here's a dramatic example. A teenager was in a car accident that killed her friends and left her in a coma. She woke up with no memory of the accident, yet she began having panic attacks every time she heard laughter. It seems that she was laughing in the back seat at the time of the accident. Her brain connected the pain of the impact with the sound of laughter. Now, her brain tried to warn her of the danger when it heard laughter. She didn't consciously think laughing causes car crashes. But big pain builds big pathways, which turn on a big chemical sense of threat.

The girl withdrew from the world because she feared hearing laughter. But with help, she taught her brain that you don't actually die when cortisol makes it feel that way. The teenager with the alcohol habit taught his brain that you don't actually die when social fear triggers cortisol. You can teach your brain that you don't actually die when you depart from your old self-soothing strategy. You can learn to notice your internal emergency alarm without rushing into old relief habits. At first, it may feel like you will die if you don't do something when the "do something!" feeling turns on. But you build a new pathway if you feed your brain a new experience repeatedly.

The first step is to recognize the feeling as an old cortisol pathway rather than a fact. The next step is to do something you like for twenty to forty minutes while your body eliminates the cortisol, choosing from your pantry of sustainable self-soothers. Finally, you can stimulate happy chemicals by taking steps to relieve the underlying problem instead of just distracting yourself from it. Let's look closer at these steps.

Start by identifying your old cortisol pathways. The word "trauma" is widely used here, but your goal is not to label yourself as "traumatized." Your goal is to see how your sense of threat fits old pathways so you know your role in creating it. This is hard to do because we are designed to honor our own alarm system. You trust your own cortisol because it has protected you from getting burned or run over for years. You expect it to protect you from social threats too. So when you get a whiff of cortisol, you want to do whatever makes it stop. In that moment, you can be ready with a new self-soothing tool instead of rushing for an unsustainable self-soothing habit. But what?

New choices often seem unappealing because they're not yet connected to positive expectations. **Fortunately, you can build positive expectations for a new self-soothing tool with repetition. There is no one right self-soothing tool. It's right for you if it distracts you from threatening thoughts without harmful long-term consequences.** We can all benefit from trying out new self-soothing habits. Let's explore some options.

A walk in the park is one we hear about a lot, but if you spend the walk arguing in your head with people who annoy you, it just triggers more cortisol. Yoga is often recommended for self-soothing, but if you  spend your yoga time getting frustrated with your body, it just triggers more cortisol. Reading and watching movies are popular self-soothing techniques, but if you choose stressful stories, you end up with more cortisol. Preparing healthy food is another well-known soother, but if you spend the time worrying about toxins in the food, it's not soothing.

Your goal is to find an activity that you truly enjoy that does not have harmful consequences. Activities that use your mind and body together are good at distracting from negative thoughts, such as crafts, gardening, and playing a musical instrument. You could also walk in the park or do yoga if you learn to keep your mind out of negative territory while you're doing it. I listen to an audiobook during my walk, and I carefully choose positive content. Video games and cross-word puzzles work for many people, but they do not use your body very much, so they can leave you tense. Experiment with new self-soothers when you're in a good mood so they're ready for you when you're in a bad mood. With repetition, a new pathway will build and the new choice will feel normal.

Distraction is not your end goal, of course. It's just a tool for lowering your cortisol so you can take your next step. Your goal is to trigger happy chemicals in sustainable ways and stop triggering them in unsustainable ways. Fortunately, you will trigger happy chemicals when you step toward solutions to the problem that triggered your cortisol. That's how our brain works!

You don't always know what triggered your cortisol, and sometimes there is no problem. You just feel bad because you saw a pattern of cues that matched a threat from your past. Here is a personal example. When I was a kid, my mother flew into a rage if I spilled a drink. I did not want to be a person who raged over spilled milk, so I worked on building new responses. But one day, I spilled a drink and a scream came out of my mouth. It wasn't a scream of anger– it  was the scream of a fearful child. I didn't even notice that I screamed, but my kids noticed. They hadn't heard that noise come out of me before, so it surprised them. I was surprised that they were surprised, because the noise was so small compared to what I grew up with. Seeing it through their eyes helped me understand the power of old pathways.

As my knowledge of the brain grew, I got interested in my mother's old pathways. When she was young, her family was short of food money, so spilled milk meant real hunger. To make matters worse, my mother was responsible for feeding her younger sisters when she was quite young herself. Suddenly, I saw that her reaction to spills was an old cortisol pathway.

Whether your cortisol is a false alarm or a real threat, you can feel good by taking a step toward meeting your needs. You have to understand your needs in order to do that. When you know what triggers happy chemicals, and how the un-met need predominates, you can design steps that trigger good feelings.

You may hesitate to take a step because you fear failure. Past failure wired you to avoid new steps. But you deprive yourself of happy chemicals if you wait for a risk-free course of action. So choose your best next step knowing that failure is just cortisol that you can relieve.

Recognizing your old cortisol patterns is a big help. You can see how they filter your facts, which frees you to find new perspectives. Your cortisol pathways were built when you were a powerless child with limited options. If you rip off the cortisol goggles, you can reexamine the situation from the perspective of adult strength rather than childhood weakness. You may not feel strong. You may not think you have options. But you can find the cortisol circuits that create these thoughts and then see what the world looks like without them.

Your mammal brain sees every obstacle as a threat, so you will always have threats to manage. You will always look for threats because that's how our brain promotes survival. But you can learn to focus on your next step and enjoy happy chemicals. A gazelle survives by focusing on the path in front of it instead of on the lion. You will feel good when you focus on the path in front of you.

A gazelle is never completely safe because it always lives in a world full of predators. But a gazelle is not "traumatized." It has confidence in its next step. A gazelle cannot wait for a perfect world before it goes out to meet its needs. It trusts its ability to manage whatever comes along. You can do the same. You may lose your job, your partner may leave you, and world events may affect you in unexpected ways. Whatever happens, you will have endless suffering if you flow into old cortisol pathways. But you have the power to change course with your self-soothing tool and your next step.

MAKE IT HAPPEN

Complete these exercises to understand the power of your old cortisol pathways.

o **Think of three bad moments in your youth. Now look at your present pain and see how the patterns overlap.**

_____

_____

_____

o **What did you do to relieve a bad feeling when you were young? What did those around you** do? How do you feel about those behaviors and thought patterns today?

_____

_____

_____

o Think of something you hate and urgently want to avoid. Can you find the early experience that matches this impulse?

_____

_____

_____

Day 11

YOUR DOPAMINE FUTURE

Today, you will:
- explore new paths to dopamine
- design a new dopamine habit that you'd like to have
- build a new dopamine habit by making a plan to repeat a new thought or action

You can enjoy the excitement of dopamine by focusing on what you <u>can</u> do instead of what you can't do.

A small step toward a reward is enough to trigger the joy of dopamine. You only get a bit, and it's gone quickly, but you can trigger more by taking another step. Each step builds the pathway that helps you expect a reward from that action. A reward is anything that meets a need. You define rewards with old pathways, but you can build new pathways to enjoy new rewards.

Dopamine evolved to help us climb toward distant goals instead of only grabbing low-hanging fruit. So choose a goal that doesn't hurt you in the long run and start stepping.

You must see yourself getting closer to the goal to trigger dopamine. Imagine you're climbing a mountain, but you can't see the peak due to clouds. You know you're getting closer anyway because you know that your steps have power.

Realistic expectations are important. If your expectations are too high, you won't see yourself approaching the reward, so you won't trigger dopamine. Low expectations are also a problem because your brain habituates to what you already have. Climbing the same mountain every day does not trigger dopamine. Look for ways to meet an un-met need with steps you can actually take. Build on the pathways you have instead of expecting to be a completely different person.

You may feel lost when you set a new course, but your knowledge of the brain is your roadmap. It guides you to:

- Choose a reward that's relevant to your survival needs because that's what triggers dopamine.
- Divide a big goal into small chunks so you can always see yourself making progress.
- Give yourself an immediate reward for those first few steps toward a distant goal.

Let's look closer at these strategies.

First, let's think about triggering new dopamine by meeting your survival needs in new ways. This is hard to make sense of since you are not consciously thinking about survival, and you're wired by the rewards of your past. But you can build onto your old wiring while finding new ways to meet physical or social needs. Here is a simple example.

A man we'll call "Joe" loved motorcycle racing. It gave him a skill he was proud of (serotonin), camaraderie (oxytocin), and new goals to reach (dopamine). Joe started training for another race whenever he felt bad about something. It worked until he got a head injury. Then he had to stop. Now, he feels like he has lost everything. He wishes he had a new passion, but how can you fake passion?

Joe solves the problem by thinking of it in terms of dopamine, serotonin, and oxytocin. He looks for an activity that provides social support, social recognition, and a realistic new goal. Nothing seems right, so he samples many different activities. At first, nothing excites him. But he is surprised to find two separate activities that meet two different needs– one brings pride and another brings friendship. Both trigger dopamine when he plans them. In time, Joe's **rewards multiply because the pride activity leads to new social bonds, and the social-support activity leads to a new skill he's proud of.** So he ends up with two new passions that meet his needs! Each time he participates, the pathway builds and starts to feel "normal."

It takes more than hobbies to meet your needs, of course. Often, it feels like a huge mountain is blocking the path to meeting your needs. You don't see how you can climb the mountain with the skills you have. If you break big challenges into smaller parts, you can move forward and enjoy the dopamine. Let's see how it worked for a woman we'll call "Jo."

Jo hates her job. She doesn't see how she can get a better job, so she feels stuck. She spends a lot of time complaining, which builds her cortisol pathway. Then she learns about her brain. She sees that she can reach big goals in small steps and feel good along the way. So she designs a plan to find a new job in small steps. **She makes it realistic by focusing on steps within her control instead of on things outside her control.**

Jo decides to start her plan by gathering information about career skills. She sets a goal of interviewing one person a day about their career skills for two weeks. Then she plans to build her job skills with online course. She sets a goal of one hour a night on these courses for three months. After that, she commits to spending a half hour a night applying for new jobs, for as long as it takes.

Jo felt great while creating this plan. Her dopamine flowed because she started expecting to reach a reward. In the past, she expected disappointment, so cortisol undermined her. She changed that by designing steps she knew she could take. Each time she reached her daily goal, more dopamine was stimulated. She saw herself approaching the goal, which built a pathway that anticipated success instead of failure.

It's hard to get started when the goal seems far away. To make it easier, plan an immediate reward for steps toward your goal. Treating yourself trains your brain to feel good now about a path that will not feel good until the future. You can find healthy immediate rewards if you look beyond old habits. **Twenty minutes of "me time" for a desired activity is a great reward.** I once rewarded myself with twenty minutes of a Spanish soap opera that had seventy-five full-hour episodes. I got my work done because I couldn't wait to watch more. My Spanish improved too!

You can use food rewards in a healthy way. Cook a delicious treat from healthy ingredients and freeze it in small pieces. Enjoy one piece after you reach your daily goal. Do not eat it until you reach that goal!

Another healthy reward is the act of seeking. Our brain evolved to seek, so you stimulate the excitement of dopamine when you scan for something new. Whether you're browsing new restaurants or walking in the woods, you activate your natural seeking system. Searching for new music or new knowledge stimulates it, which is why internet surfing is so enticing. Going to a museum activates your natural scanning system. So does shopping, though it's not sustainable.

Variety makes your reward more rewarding, so experiment with a variety of ways to treat yourself.

Repetition will build a dopamine pathway, so you will expect to feel good when you take steps to meet your needs. You will build a new sense of wellbeing.

Of course there will be obstacles, setbacks, and disappointments. That's why it's good to set three goals– a long-term, short-term, and middle-term goal.

Then, when one path is blocked, you can focus on another. You will always have a way to step forward and stimulate dopamine. Always design one goal that you can reach by the end of the day.

You might reject this plan. You might insist that it won't work. Past disappointments make it easy to think that, but you can manage that cortisol with the skills you learned yesterday.

Another reason for dismissing this plan is the bad image of dopamine. We hear a lot about its role in addiction, whether substance abuse, social media addiction, or compulsive behaviors. We rarely hear about the natural healthy function of dopamine. Thus, we come to associate dopamine with undesirable behavior and overlook our need for its motivating power in daily life.

Yet another reason for rejecting a new path to dopamine is the fear of losing your reliable source of serotonin. For example, when you try a new sport or cook a new dish, you may not be "good at it." You risk losing that one-up position when you embark on a new path to dopamine. Alternatively, you might say  it's "selfish" to focus on your own needs. This allows you to avoid scary new steps while believing that you are a superior person serving the greater good. Sometimes, you have to develop new serotonin pathways to support your new dopamine pathway.

Your reliable oxytocin pathways may also be challenged by your new path to dopamine. When you try a new activity, you may lose the pals you had in an old activity. If you got rewards by sticking with a group in the past, you might feel like you'd lose something by charting your own course. If others met your needs for you in the past, you fear losing that by designing your own steps to meet needs.

You will miss out on the joy of dopamine if you allow these concerns to divert you from stepping toward goals. You don't have to sacrifice one chemical to enjoy another because there are so many ways to trigger each of them.

You can enjoy more dopamine by creating a plan to reward yourself in the short run for steps that are good for you in the long run. A small step is all it takes to get your dopamine going. Your step creates positive expectations about your next step, so you will want to keep stepping. Believing in the power of your own steps is a learned skill. If you didn't learn it yesterday, you can learn it today.

MAKE IT HAPPEN

Complete these exercises to design your new dopamine pathways.

o **Think of a short-run goal, a long-run goal, and a middle-term goal.**

_____

_____

_____

o Think of something that frustrates you, and design realistic steps to fix it. Be sure to focus on your own life rather than global abstractions.

_____

_____

_____

o List seeking activities that you enjoy. The next time you feel bad, spend 20-40 minutes on one of these activities.

_____

_____

_____

YOUR OXYTOCIN FUTURE

Today you will learn to:
o **repeat small steps toward social trust**
o **repair broken trust to relieve cortisol**
o **build positive expectations about social support**

Your inner mammal is always looking for support you can trust. It's great to know that trust builds in small steps. Each time you give and receive trust, an oxytocin pathway builds, making it easier to turn it on the next time. So how can you give and receive trust?

Doing it consciously feels strange because most of our trust pathways build without conscious thought. A simple example is the friendship that forms between freshman roommates. Small moments of trust build big oxytocin pathways when they're repeated over time. Similar bonds may build between people who share an office, though it's harder after the myelin years.

Another oxytocin bond that builds without conscious intent is the rescue. **If someone rescues you from a real threat, you surge with oxytocin because you have gotten real protection and support**. The big surge builds a big pathway, so you feel like you can count on that person– even if you actually cannot. The same is true if you rescue someone else from danger. They get wired to see you as a hero. You may not feel like a hero, or even intend to rescue them in the future, but big chemicals build big pathways.

Bonds built by accidents of experience cannot be counted on to fill your life with social trust. Fortunately, you can build new oxytocin bonds by feeding your brain new inputs about social trust. It's like learning a foreign language– it takes a lot of repetition and it feels strange because you don't realize how much repetition it took to learn your native language. Let's explore some ways of teaching your brain the social-trust language that feels right for you.

You cannot control other people, of course, so you have to focus on steps within your control. You can plan new steps to offer support to others, and graciously receive any support that's offered. Here are some simple examples of small steps toward social trust:

- listening to a person
- lending a hand without taking over
- honoring your commitment to someone
- seeing a situation from their perspective
- respecting a person who helps you instead of being hostile.

Here is a simple example. Imagine a neighbor whom you've never met. You have a bad feeling about them because old negative expectations turn on. You decide to take small steps toward them: eye contact, a smile, an offer of help. You do not get upset if they do not reciprocate immediately. You do not take it personally since you cannot know their old circuits. You allow time for them to respond in their own way. Meanwhile, you take small initiatives with others. One

 small initiative a day means you're planting many seeds, and some will sprout at a future time that you can't predict. One day, one person will step toward you, and another day, another person. You will keep responding with small steps.

You don't have to spend money to build trust; you have to spend energy. You don't have to give up yourself to build oxytocin circuits; you just have to bridge the gap between your needs and the needs of others. You can't control the way others respond to your overtures, and that can be frustrating. But you can stay focused on building your side of different bridges, and in time, some people will build back toward you. You can't predict when or how, but you will have nice surprises if you keep building. Eventually, you will have a web of social support.

A web is the modern adult form of support. It's not the support you have as a child or a member of a traditional tribe. It allows you to live independently while still easing your inner mammal's fear of isolation. A web does not support you every minute, but you trust it to be there when  you need it. **Your oxytocin depends on your own trust in your own web.**

You may be thinking "I have already done enough! Others must do their share!" This is a widespread thought pattern because we are not objective judges of the support we give and receive. Sometimes you give in a way that meets your needs but does not actually meet the needs of others. Sometimes you get support but you do not notice it because you are focused on the next potential threat.

It's not realistic to expect others to make you feel supported all the time. Unrealistic expectations are an obstacle to oxytocin. They cause disappointment with the support you have and hold you back from steps toward new trust. You can enjoy more oxytocin if you feed your brain more realistic expectations.

It's realistic to remember that we are all mammals. We all want support to promote our own survival. The urge for support is basically selfish, but you have to manage selfish impulses to earn trust from others. You have to give support to get support.

You won't do this if you expect to fail. **Positive expectations are what motivate you to give and receive trust. But your expectations need to be realistic in order to stay positive. This is the challenge we all grapple with in order to enjoy the oxytocin reward.** Let's look closer at positive but realistic expectations about social trust.

Let's say you think someone has let you down or dislikes you. Instead of dwelling on facts that support this interpretation, you can look for other possible explanations. Old lenses are always filtering our facts, but you are free to try out new lenses. You may have new insights that lead to new trust. Then, oxytocin will pave a new pathway.

A fast track to trust would be nice. The slow track is frustrating, so it's useful to remember why the mammal brain makes careful decisions about when to trust. If someone bought you a car, you would not necessarily trust them, even if you accepted the car. Grand gestures do not build instant trust because people learn from experience that big steps are rarely sustainable. Big gestures get attention, but they do not necessarily overcome the cortisol of distrust.

Distrust is a cortisol pathway built from past experience. Cortisol tells you that it's not safe to lower your guard with this person, as much as you'd want the oxytocin. You can repair broken trust in small steps to relieve the cortisol of being on bad terms with someone. Start with tiny steps so that neither of you feels threatened. In time, take another tiny step. You will feel great when they reciprocate. **Do not expect immediate results.** Meanwhile, take steps toward others to keep building your web.

It's realistic to remember that a monkey who gives a grooming rarely gets an immediate grooming in return. It often gets a different form of reciprocation at a different time. The monkey brain keeps score, and decides whether to keep grooming an individual who disappoints them or invest effort elsewhere. We keep score too, though we hate to admit it. **We are not objective judges of reciprocity, alas. You easily remember the disappointments you experienced, and forget the times you disappointed others.**

Everyone has disappointments in their past, so your quest for oxytocin brings your old disappointment network into contact with another person's old disappointment network. These old pathways sift our information, but you can take off the cortisol goggles and see new information. You can accept the fact that your inner mammal wants protection to promote your survival, and others want protection to promote their survival. If you are shocked by this, you will flood your life with cortisol. It's better to accept the mammalian impulses beneath the flowery language used for social bonding.

You can't control the trust of others, but if you control your own steps, your side of the bridge gets built. In time, you will have bridges with many people. You will stimulate oxytocin because you are trusting others and seeing yourself as a person worthy of trust.

You should not expect support

from everyone all the time. It's not realistic. You will fail to get the support you want sometimes, and cortisol will make it feel like a threat. Your verbal brain will try to help by looking for evidence, and it finds evidence when it looks. Pathways will build that zoom in on that evidence in the future. You can easily end up convinced that people are against you.

If you look for patterns in these feelings, you will see how you are reactivating disappointments of your past. Instead, you could be feeding your brain new inputs and building new expectations.

Feed your brain the realistic idea that your fellow mammal wants to trust as much as you do, but fears disappointment as much as you do. Their hopes and fears are different, of course, because they built them from their own experience. When you expect disappointment, you don't take the steps necessary to build trust. When you expect rewards from small steps, then you keep stepping.

Dopamine rewards you for stepping toward oxytocin, which is why people get excited about a "big date" or acceptance into a new group. Serotonin rewards you for getting support from an important person. The happy chemicals work together to help you enjoy the good feeling of social support.

It's hard to sustain expectations that are both positive and realistic. Sometimes we're too positive and sometimes we're too too negative. Let's look closer at both.

It's easy to be too positive because idealized views of social bonds are popular. We hear talk of "unconditional support," which creates the idea that other people get this so you should too. Words like "empathy" and "altruism" create glorified but unrealistic expectations about social trust. Biological facts are filtered in ways that make it seem like animals have perfect harmony. Our lives fall short of these idealized expectations, so it seems like we're missing out.

Conversely, it's easy to be too negative about social trust because childhood disappointments get myelinated. Those pathways tell you "no one accepts me," and wire you to look for evidence of rejection, criticism, and hostility. **Everyone has disappointments, whether they got a lot of support in their youth, or a little. If you got a lot of support, you have to adjust to the adult fact that reciprocity is expected. If you got little support, you have to learn the habit of giving and receiving it.** Everyone ends up in the same place, fearing a lack of support, because the mammal brain does that.

It's hard to stay realistic. When someone smiles at you, it's easy to hope that they will love you forever and rescue you from your misery...or at least buy your screenplay and make you rich. When someone lends you a hand, your inner mammal hopes they will stand by your side forever and help you conquer the world. You expect a new lover to agree with you on everything. You expect a new boss to be amazed by your talent. You expect a new neighbor to

be your ally in your war with the world. Disappointment is inevitable. But you can learn to notice your expectations and take one step toward social trust before lunch, and another after dinner. The good feeling of letting down your guard will turn on.

It's hard to do this, so shortcuts are popular.

Going to a stadium and cheering for a team or entertainer is a popular shortcut. It gives you an instant bond with thousands of people. When the game or concert is over, those people will not be there for you, and you will not be there for them. But you get an oxytocin moment because our ancestors found safety in numbers. We like the feeling of being in a large herd, but we don't like being tied down to a herd, so we create temporary herds that stimulate temporary trust. The modern world allows you to design your own trust network instead of forcing you to commit to one tribe. **But if you don't build your own trust network, you don't have one.**

Pets are another popular shortcut. We are told that pets stimulate oxytocin, but animals cannot support

you the way humans can. If you give up on humans, your real support needs are not met. As much as you may love the pet, you feel like

something is missing. You can fix it by repeating small steps of trust toward humans.

A very popular oxytocin shortcut is bonding around bad habits. People who share your bad habit make you feel safe. Of course, you'd get more sustainable support from people who avoid that habit, but your old circuits see them as a threat. So you bond with people who support your unsustainable habit, making it harder to break.

Spending money is a well-known oxytocin shortcut. Imagine that you buy an expensive dinner or birthday gift for someone. You may say you had no expectations, but unconscious expectations are often disappointed. Cortisol surges and makes it harder to trust in the future. You would be better off with small acts of trust, repeated over time.

Politics is another popular oxytocin shortcut. You tell yourself it serves the greater good, but it serves your own good by creating the illusion of social support. Politics focuses on common enemies, which builds instant bonds among everyone on "our side." Serotonin boosts the reward because our side feels superior. Dopamine rewards you when your group confirms its own predictions about the fate of humanity.

But you pay a high price for the political path to oxytocin. You fear enemies all the time. And you fear losing your herd if you fail to follow at all times. They may even brand you as an "enemy" if you fail to conform. You could join another political cause, but the same thing will happen. You can avoid this dilemma by building your own web of one-to-one trust bonds.

If you expect trust to come effortlessly, you will not do what it takes to create it. If you blame others for failing to support you, you will not take the steps. Many people want more oxytocin but they don't take the steps.

Your inner mammal is always making decisions about where to invest your limited energy. You are always deciding which bridges to build, and others are doing the same. Everyone cannot invest in everyone else, so if you expect that, you get disappointed. Instead, you can celebrate your power to decide whom to step toward, and what step to take. You decide whose fur you will groom. You cannot control the responses of others, but you can control your next step.

MAKE IT HAPPEN

Complete these exercises to design your new oxytocin pathways.

o **Think of a small way to build trust with someone, and do it before lunch. Do not buy them something! Do not expect an immediate reward. Just notice your own good feelings.**

_____

_____

_____

o **Commit to making one small act of trust each day for 45 days. Give trust and receive trust on alternate days. You can give trust by being helpful or having a positive expectation about a person. You can receive trust by acting trustworthy, to help them build a positive expectation of you.**

_____

_____

_____

o **Plan an event that offers trust-building opportunities. Notice your feelings as you plan–**

both the fear of disappointment and the excitement of approaching a reward.

Day 13

YOUR SEROTONIN FUTURE

Today you will learn how to:
o **create healthy one-up feelings**
o **manage one-down feelings**
o **accept the one-up urge in everyone**

You crave the good feeling of social importance whether you want to or not. There is no easy way to get it, and disappointment feels surprisingly bad. You can end up feeling threatened a lot, though your life is safer than your ancestors' wildest dreams. Fortunately, there is a better way.

The solution is to give your inner mammal what it wants in sustainable ways. You can give yourself a feeling of importance instead of expecting the world to give it to you. This may seem arrogant or stupid or sad. We prefer recognition from others instead of giving it to ourselves. But chasing the world's applause is not sustainable. It leads to cortisol, which tempts you to make it stop in harmful ways.

Carving your own path to social importance is a skill you can learn. It's scary at first. Just thinking about your social standing can trigger one-down circuits from your past. It may seem like you have two bad choices– between endless striving and hopeless giving up. **But you can carve a middle path by being important in your own mind.** You can wire in a kinder, gentler way to feel one-up.

You may say you're above all this silly posturing for prominence. You may feel superior to people who need that. But when you see others get ahead in some way, your cortisol turns on. You end up resenting – even hating – people who get social recognition. The cortisol hurts you, and you release more every time you see status seekers get rewards.

You may insist that you do not think about social dominance at all. But **our brain focuses on the *unmet* need. When your other needs are met, the urge for status grabs your attention.** In the past, people spent more energy finding food and water, so they had less energy for serotonin-seeking. Today, people can pour themselves into a quest for glory. This makes every opportunity seem urgent, and every obstacle seem like a crisis.

Your verbal brain struggles to explain these strong feelings. It mirrors the explanations of people you respect. You may be reproducing their serotonin-seeking habits, and their cortisol, without realizing it. You are better off designing your own way to manage your natural social-comparison impulse. You can blaze a new trail between the extremes of too much status-seeking and too little.

If you try to be the dominant monkey all the time, no one will want to be near you and someday a bigger monkey will probably hurt you. But if you see yourself as a dominated little monkey, you miss out on serotonin. Fortunately, you can enjoy sustainable serotonin if you stick to the middle lane and steer clear of the fast lane and the slow lane.

Life in the middle lane means finding healthy ways to satisfy your mammalian urge for social importance. No one learns this formally because the mammal brain is not widely understood. But you can learn it today.

Step One is to notice your social-comparison thoughts and accept your natural urge for the one-up feeling. Step Two is to build healthy serotonin pathways by feeding your brain healthy thoughts about social comparison. Step Three is to repeat so the new pathway flows.

A healthy one-up thought is one that puts you up without putting others down. For example, if I knit a

scarf, I can take pride in my scarf. I don't have to sneer at the scarves of others. I don't have to imagine others sneering at my scarf. If I hear criticism from my inner voice, I can remind myself that I created it instead of blaming "them." In truth, my knitting may be flawed, and I can improve it by learning from others. But I can be real about my own feelings as I do that.

Of course, there are people who look for flaws in other people's knitting. But I don't need to focus on them. They may enjoy a serotonin moment when they find fault with others, but that wires them to focus on fault-finding. They live in a world of constant criticism. I can choose differently for myself. I can focus on pride in my own skills. I can manage my own brain instead of trying to manage other people's brains.

It's hard to see the good in your own knitting sometimes. Thinking well of yourself violates a taboo learned by many, so it triggers your cortisol. But you also enjoy a drip of serotonin when you take pride in your actions, and that makes it easier to act again. Each step you're proud of triggers more serotonin. With repetition, a new pathway grows big enough to compete with the old one. You don't have to spend your life focused on your flaws.

Realism is important. If your knitting is terrible, you can take pride in correcting your mistakes. The goal is not to put yourself up in a false way. That would not be sustainable. **The goal is to feel confidence in your own skills, because that's what makes your inner mammal feel safe.**

No matter where you are in life, you can be happy if you learn to manage your social-comparison impulse. You can learn to give your inner mammal the one-up position without dominating others. More important, **you can learn to feel safe in one-down moments instead of feeling threatened. You won't flip-flop between the extremes of grandiosity and despair when you can give yourself the recognition you long for.**

Ups and downs are inevitable on the road to serotonin. Some people in your life won't appreciate your new one-up thoughts. They may have liked it when you put yourself down. They are status-seeking mammals just like you. Conflict is part of every mammal's life, but you can navigate it by putting yourself up without putting others down.

It's nicer to get recognition from others than to give it to yourself, of course. But if you wait for the world to applaud you, you will never take action. And you have to take action before you can get applause.

 You have to do something useful before people notice. And they may not notice for a long time. Most of history's great achievers were not appreciated while they were alive. If they had waited for recognition, they would not have done anything. The comforts of modern life rest on efforts that did not win approval when they were made.

People who do get public recognition usually get attacked as well. Mammals attack those with status in order to raise their own status. Your life would not get easier if your status rose. You would just substitute one threatened feeling for another. You are better off learning to manage your threatened feelings. If you rely on public opinion for your sense of worth, you will not take the steps necessary to build a realistic sense of worth.

It may seem like VIPs get to be one-up all the time, but if you were in their head, you would see it differently. You'd see their fear of losing what they have, and the way they habituate to what they have so it stops exciting them. They need new recognition to spark their serotonin, just like everyone else. Being a big shot would not make you happy all the time. It's not worth your effort.

It may seem like "saving the world" would give you endless serotonin, but it would not. Your inner m a m m a l w o u l d compare you to other world-savers, and notice when they get more recognition than you get. Your urge for recognition would still be disappointed some times. Your happiness  would still depend on your ability to manage one-down feelings.

No one gets a free pass to serotonin. The challenge is daunting, so shortcuts are popular. Shortcuts are habits that relieve one-down feelings fast, the way junk food relieves hunger fast. You can think of it as "junk status." Like junk food, junk status hurts you in the long run, but you crave it in the short run. There are endless forms of junk status, and each generation develops new ones as new technologies emerge.

 Social media comes to mind today, but it's useful to observe the junk status of generations past. In the 1800s, a small waist was the popular status symbol and people suffered terribly to have a small waist. In the 1700s, people strove to wear the biggest wig. Before that, people strove to build the biggest castle or the biggest pyramid. Each brain learns from what gets recognition in the world around it.

Other popular forms of junk status include telling off your boss, rescuing your children, and taking pride in your ability to hold your liquor. However you learn to feel important, you build a pathway to repeat that behavior even if it hurts you in the long run.

The solution to junk status is the same as the solution to junk food: stock up on healthy treats. With a bit of planning, you can be ready with healthy ways to treat yourself to serotonin. **You can create something you are proud of, or build a skill that you are proud of. Your new source of pride builds a pathway that diverts you from rushing into junk.**

You have probably heard that helping others is the key to happiness. People who present themselves as helpers or rescuers get public praise, so mirror neurons make this seem like the way to go. But maybe you have tried this already and ended up feeling bad. That's because it tells your inner mammal that other people matter and you don't. It feels one-down, so you may seek relief in junk status. There is another way: give your inner mammal a feeling of importance instead of only thinking others are important.

A great way to feel one-up is to create something that lasts. Your body will not last, and your big human brain knows that. Animals are not aware of their own mortality, but the human cortex enables you to imagine a future that you will not be part of. You terrorize your inner mammal with this knowledge. The bad feeling eases when you create something that will survive when you are gone. A carpenter who makes a good chair creates something that will survive. It's just a chair, but it soothes the inner

mammal's fear of its own demise.

Humans have always worked to create things that last because it relieves cortisol and stimulates serotonin. We create children, art, technology, organizations, and knowledge that we expect to survive when we're gone. The path to creating is full of disappointment, but people keep taking another step because pride in your creation feels good.

Having children was the primary way to create in the world before birth control. Keeping children alive took so much energy that you didn't have much left to create other things. Children came quickly after puberty, so you could easily be a grandparent in your thirties. Seeing your grandchildren mirror your traditions gave you the sense that a part of you would survive. Your serotonin surged when you imagined the status advancements of your grandchildren. Of course, any threats to their future status triggered your cortisol. You relieved that by returning to your dreams for your grandchildren's future.

Birth control has broadened our options for defining our legacy and investing our energy. **But we still have strong feelings about our legacy, even if we don't think this consciously. You can see how hard people strive to raise the status of their creation, even if it's just a chair.** The serotonin soon passes so they strive again and again. We care about our legacy with all the energy that animals invest in keeping their genes alive. Natural selection built a brain that rewards you with happy chemicals when you do things that promote the survival of your unique individual essence.

You don't need to be a king with a castle to create something that lasts. A teacher who inspires a child has a lasting impact. A cook who invents a recipe creates something lasting. A plumber who lays pipe creates something lasting. **Take pride in what you build and you'll relieve threatened feelings while sparking serotonin.**

Plumbers often criticize the work of other plumbers. Cooks often critique the cooking of others. Teachers often condemn the teaching of others. Creators compare their work to others, and long to believe their work is superior. They feel unfairly deprived of recognition, because the mammal brain goes there. This fills your life with cortisol if you let it. But you can learn to take pride in your own creation without putting down the creations of others. Just keep redirecting your mind to that next step toward building something you're proud of.

Each step with pride builds the pathway that makes the next step easier. When it's hard, you can reward yourself with healthy treats to build positive associations. **You can make peace with your status-seeking impulse instead of getting upset about the status seeking of others.**

You may still condemn this as "ego." You may still hate people who feel important and insist that you don't care about such things. But whatever your verbal brain says, your mammal brain compares you to others and responds with happy or unhappy chemicals. If you don't manage this consciously, your old pathways will manage it. You will seek status in ways that worked in your past, even if it hurts you today. You will think others are putting you down because you don't see how you are putting yourself down. You can replace those old thought loops by feeding your brain new inputs.

MAKE IT HAPPEN

Complete these exercises to design your new serotonin pathways.

o Think of a step you can take that you're proud of and take it today. Then plan the next step.

_____

_____

_____

o Generate a list of steps that you're proud of. When you feel one-down, look at your list and take one of these steps.

_____

_____

o **Make a plan to repeat a step you're proud of every day. Use healthy treats to build positive associations until it feels natural.**

DESIGN YOUR SUSTAINABLE PATH

Today you will learn how to:
o **blaze a new trail in your brain**
o **choose the trail that's right for you**
o **keep going until it flows**

You can blaze a new trail to your happy chemicals by repeating a new choice until the neurons connect. A lot of repetition is needed for a new path to grow big enough to compete with an old one. You flow more easily with each repetition, though the old circuit is always there to tempt you.

You have to define your new trail in order to repeat it. Targeting something you already like makes it easier to get started because you already have some connection to your happy chemicals. What do you like that's also sustainable? This is a challenge, but you can meet the challenge because you understand your brain.

To succeed, focus on one new trail at a time. Start with something small to build confidence in your neuroplasticity. Then you can tackle your big challenge. If it's still hard, break that big challenge into smaller chunks and tackle one at a time. My dentist got me to floss my teeth by making me promise to floss just one tooth a day.

A great way to build a new pathway is to repeat your new choice for 45 days and reward yourself on the last day. If you miss a day, start over so you have 45 straight days of no excuses. On Day 45, you will be so happy with your new neural pathway that you will want to build another!

You can stop your bad habit by replacing it with a new habit. Think of your old habit as a highway in your brain. You need to build a new highway, and also an exit ramp to get you from the old path to the new one. When you feel bad, you will flow into your self-soothing strategy if you carefully design it and repeat it.

Maybe you still think it shouldn't be so hard. **Maybe you still think happy chemicals flow effortlessly in others and you want that too.** These beliefs are tempting, but now you know the facts. Happy chemicals don't last. Each spurt soon passes, and we all have to do more to get more. We all use old pathways to seek them, until we build new pathways.

Are you thinking that you got stuck with bad pathways and others have an easier road to happiness? It's natural to compare yourself to others even though you don't know their whole story. But focusing on others wastes energy that you could have spent blazing your own trails. Here's a simple story that will help you do that.

Five teenage boys played in a band and dreamed of being "big." They auditioned for a famous band, but only one of them was hired. The other four responded in four different ways.

One of them surged with cortisol every time he looked at his guitar, so he put it away and never looked at it again. This taught his brain to manage cortisol by avoiding things. He avoided a lot.

The second boy kept his dream alive by going to parties and gushing about the great band he will play in some day. That felt good, so he partied more. He practiced while high, and thought he sounded great. As the years went by, no one would work with him except other intoxicated people. He was not getting closer to the dream, so it stopped triggering his dopamine. Partying sparked his dopamine, so he focused on that. He died young.

The third boy decided to get serious about his music career. But he anticipated rejection every time he had an audition. He imagined getting laughed at by the people he's auditioning for, and started hating them. Just thinking about auditioning sparked his cortisol, which made it harder to play. **He got a moment of relief by using the word "idiot" for anyone with the power to hire him.** But his cortisol surged a lot, and made his hands shake. He decided that something was wrong with his hands. He went to the doctor, but they didn't find anything. He decided to be a singer so his hand-shaking wouldn't matter. But his unchecked cortisol eroded his singing voice and his health. Now he sings on the couch in his parents' basement.

The fourth boy decided to improve his skills by taking lessons. He also took a course on mental preparation for auditions. He did all the homework, but he failed seven auditions. Finally, a minor band accepted him, and he was thrilled. The band didn't make money, though, so he started giving music lessons to support himself. He worked hard to communicate effectively with his students and their parents. They valued his skill, and word-of-mouth spread. He stayed focused on the next step toward meeting his needs, and that trained his brain to expect rewards if he focused on the next step. Now he owns a big music school that brings pleasure to many families.

You are always training your brain with your thoughts and actions. You can choose thoughts and actions that pave happy pathways instead of threat pathways.

In the past two weeks, you learned what it takes to trigger happy chemicals in this brain we've inherited. You found out why our chemicals depend on old pathways, and how we can tailor them with repetition. Now you are ready to blaze new trails to happy chemicals by focusing on your next step.

You may say this is not a good time because you are going through a rough patch. But life is full of rough patches, and happy chemicals are there to help. There is no one right way. You can design the happy-chemical pathway that's right for you. Here is a story that will help.

Four women lose their job in a company cutback. Cortisol surges in each of them, but each finds her way back to happy chemicals by building onto her unique individual pathways.

The first woman decides to cut her spending to make sure that her savings last until she finds a new

job. But every time she tries to resist a purchase, her cortisol surges. She knows that she's activating old circuits built from hardships in her youth. But when the bad feeling turns on, she wants to splurge because that's what her family did when she was young. She tells herself it's fine because a good mood will help her get a job.

Fortunately, she has been learning about the brain. She knows that happy chemicals are released when you step toward meeting a need, but our brain defines "needs" with old neural pathways. She sees how her parents' reckless spending defined her "needs." She sees how she linked saving money to cortisol, even though her conscious brain knows it's good for her survival. So she decides to build a new pathway by feeding her brain new inputs. Every time she makes a money-saving choice, she stops to feel pride in her action, and to imagine herself closer to the goal. Then she rewards herself with ten minutes of reading a novel she has always wanted time for. Each week that she keeps her spending within budget, she celebrates in a way that doesn't cost anything. She feels good, and her savings last until she finds a new job.

The second woman surges with fear every time she applies for a job. She fears that a spelling mistake will disqualify her, so she checks her work over and over before hitting "Submit." As a result, she submits very few applications. Fortunately, she has been learning about her brain. She sees how the submit button triggers a fear-of-criticism pathway that she built long ago. She decides to build a new pathway linking her reward chemicals to the submit button. She sets a goal of five applications per day, and plans a reward after submitting each: a coffee after #1 (no coffee before!), a short phone call to a friend after #2, a walk after #3, a healthy meal after #4, and fun hobby time after #5. Soon, applying for jobs feels natural, and she literally forgets to panic when she hits "Submit."

The third woman reaches for her pill bottle when she hears about the layoffs. The bottle is half empty, so she focuses on stocking up since she's sure she will need it. Her doctor says she is not due for a refill, so she searches for alternatives. The quest distracts her from thinking about her future. When the pills start to wear off, she tells herself that no one will hire a pill addict who hasn't done a real day's work in years. That feels so bad that she looks for more pills. Fortunately, she has been learning about her brain.

She remembers when she first learned to distract herself from bad feelings. The sounds of family conflict reached her ears as a child, and she went out with friends to escape. Then she got high with friends, and remembers actually taking pride in her ability to escape her distress. Now, she realizes with horror that she was mirroring her family's path to pride. She sees that she needs a new way to feel special in order to give up the old way. She decides to get help since that old pathway is so deep. She gets substance abuse counseling and joins a job-hunting group. They activate her mirror neurons, which helps her take steps that spark her dopamine, serotonin and oxytocin. It feels good, so she keeps stepping. Now she has a new life that she's proud of, and new paths to happy chemicals.

The fourth woman responds to the bad news by calling ten friends and relatives. The next day, she calls them again. At first, they're supportive and tell her what she wants to hear. But by the third day, half of them don't pick up or reply. She gossips about them to the ones who do respond. The gossip becomes her daily routine, and she's proud of how well she's coping. But she doesn't take steps toward finding a job in the first month, or the second. Friends arrange interviews for her, but she treats the interviews as opportunities to gossip and get support. No job is offered.

Fortunately, this woman has been learning about her brain. She remembers getting support in a crisis when she was young, and sees how she got wired to enjoy crises instead of meeting her needs. She feels awful when she sees the pattern. She mourns the wasted years and the wasted support, yet she's terrified by the thought of doing something different. So she accepts her inner mammal with all its quirks, and starts designing the new pathway she wants to build.

She makes a plan to call one friend after completing one job application. She will have to complete five applications a day in order to call five friends. She looks for other ways to reward herself in order to preserve her friendships and enjoy variety. She likes home remodeling, so she gets out her tools and starts a project. Soon, she is earning money by helping others remodel. It's not much money, but she keeps taking steps and gets a job in a remodeling company. Soon, she is so busy that she forgets to feel alone.

You have power over your brain. You can build happy habits by taking new steps. At first, it feels

wrong because your electricity has trouble flowing along neurons that were not connected by early experience. But with planning and repetition, you can wire your happy chemicals to turn on in new ways. You can step toward greener pastures instead of just running from threats. The electricity in your brain will have a new place to flow!

MAKE IT HAPPEN

Complete these exercises to design your new pathway.

o **What new happy habit will you commit to building? Think of a small one to start with, and then tackle something important.**

_____

_____

_____

o **List some sustainable ways to reward yourself for taking a new step.**

_____

_____

_____

o Think of a new habit to help you spark each happy chemical. If it's a big change for you, how can you break it into smaller chunks?

_____

_____

_____

_____

_____

_____

_____

ABOUT THE AUTHOR

Loretta Graziano Breuning, PhD, is founder of the Inner Mammal Institute and Professor Emerita of Management at California State University, East Bay. She is the author of many personal development books, including Habits of a Happy Brain: Retrain Your Brain to Boost Your Serotonin, Dopamine, Oxytocin and Endorphin Levels.

As a teacher and a parent, she was not convinced by prevailing theories of human motivation. Then she learned about the brain chemistry we share with earlier mammals, and everything made sense. She began creating resources that have helped thousands of people make peace with their inner mammal. Her work has been translated into many languages and is cited on major media.

Dr. Breuning is a graduate of Cornell University and Tufts, and a grandparent of two. Before teaching, she worked for the United Nations in Africa.

The Inner Mammal Institute offers videos, books, podcasts, blogs, multimedia, and a training program, to help you make peace with your inner mammal. You can follow Dr. Breuning's work on most social media, YouTube, and PsychologyToday.com. Her podcast is "The Happy Brain."

Introduce your friends to their inner mammal with the free five-day happy chemical jumpstart at: InnerMammalInstitute.org.

MORE BOOKS BY

Loretta Graziano Breuning, PhD

Habits of a Happy Brain
Retrain Your Brain to Boost Your Serotonin, Dopamine, Oxytocin and Endorphin Levels

Status Games
Why We Play and How to Stop

Tame Your Anxiety
Rewiring Your Brain for Happiness

The Science of Positivity
Stop Negative Thought Patterns by Changing Your Brain Chemistry

17041019R00116